Human Resource Management in Radiology

ahra

AHRA is the premier association for imaging professionals. Since 1973, the organization has led the industry in information, education, and professional support. Its programs—including its journal, *Radiology Management*; conferences; publications; and annual meeting and exposition—establish standards of excellence throughout the profession. In addition, AHRA's Certified Radiology Administrator (CRA) program is the first and only professional credential tailored specifically for radiology administrators. The CRA is designed to elevate professional standards, enhance individual performance, and recognize administrators who demonstrate knowledge essential to the practice of radiology management. The AHRA Education Foundation supports the membership and imaging professionals in the US and abroad by granting scholarships and conducting research that enhance the effectiveness of imaging and healthcare disciplines.

Table of Contents

Acknowledgments

This project, as with the previous books in the AHRA professional development series, was successful only because of the myriad folks working behind the scenes to bring it to fruition. Bayer HealthCare Pharmaceuticals continues to receive our gratitude and sincere appreciation for their generous grant making this series of books possible. The 11 authors who contributed their time, knowledge, and expertise, as well as the peer review group who analyzed the manuscript and made suggestions to hone this project into the highly polished reference manual that resulted, are tremendously appreciated. Lynne Dodson brought her professional writing and editing skills to each chapter and was critical to the high quality of the final product. The AHRA staff, under the direction of Debra L. Murphy, Publications Manager, was critical to the meeting of deadlines on this project. Their patience and dedication was integral. We can truly say that Deb gave birth to two bundles of joy during this project, and her skills as a coach, mentor, editor, and drill sergeant cannot be understated. To all who had a hand in the completion of this book, we sincerely express our appreciation.

Lara Henshaw Archer, MBA, MS
Richard Lewis, CRA
Stephen Spearing, CRA, RT(R)

Introduction

Since the establishment of the Certified Radiology Administrator (CRA) program in 2002, almost 700 members (at the time of this printing), have stepped forward to set themselves apart by obtaining the CRA designation. The Radiology Administration Certification Commission (RACC), a self-governing body designed to oversee and maintain the integrity of the program, continues to make phenomenal strides in making the CRA designation *the* coveted designation for medical imaging management professionals.

Now, more than ever, we continue to refine the resources needed to offer reference materials for all imaging administrators to refer to and learn from. Not only to achieve the CRA designation, but to enrich their knowledge base and expand the tools necessary to complete the tasks presented to them professionally. Nowhere is this more apparent than in the domain of human resource management, especially as it relates to medical imaging.

As with the other books in the AHRA professional development series, the authors of this text represent a wide cross section of medical imaging management professionals and other experts from freestanding and hospital affiliated imaging centers; academic, community and rural hospitals; and physician practices. Human resource management continues to be one of the more challenging aspects of the profession and, accordingly, this book addresses the needs of administrators regardless of the setting.

Section 1, Human Resource Planning, reviews the impact of legal precedent on human resource practice, the challenge of building a workforce plan, and creating descriptions for those working in the area.

Section 2, Human Resource Recruitment, discusses how to find talent, the development of solid strategy and timelines, selection of appropriate compensation, and the end of the employment cycle.

Section 3, Training and Development, presents the need for orientation and continued training, along with career development, guidance in providing effective performance feedback, and the roles of coach, counselor, and mentor.

Section 4, Retention, reviews how to build solid employee relations and retain talent, as well as the communication skills necessary to improve morale and motivate teams.

Finally, the Appendices give samples for employee handbooks and human resource policies that may be adapted for your particular facility.

Technology and efficiency will continue to evolve and make various settings more state of the art; however, the human element will continue to be integral to fulfilling the mission of every organization. Changing demographics and employment patterns will demand that medical imaging administrators develop skills and expertise, along with confidence in their ability to manage an ever changing constant in the workplace—human interaction. *Human Resource Management in Radiology* is a most important tool for the medical imaging management professional and will continue to be a significant resource for the future of the profession.

Lara Henshaw Archer, MBA, MS
Richard Lewis, CRA
Stephen Spearing, CRA, RT(R)

Editors

Lara Henshaw Archer, MBA, MS
Senior Manager
RCG Healthcare Consulting
Boston, Massachusetts
Lara Henshaw Archer is a senior manager at RCG Healthcare Consulting. Ms Archer came to the RCG with significant clinical, operational, and technical experience in radiology. Prior to the Radiology Consulting Group, she worked in a number of radiology departments in the United Kingdom, including Guy's and St. Thomas' NHS Trust. Ms Archer's areas of expertise lie in clinical management, PACS, radiology information systems, and project management. She received a bachelor of science in diagnostic radiography from South Bank University in London, a master of science in information systems and a master of business administration from Northeastern University in Boston.

Richard Lewis, CRA
President and Principal Consultant
Phoenix Imaging Consultants
Orlando, Florida
Richard Lewis is the president and principal consultant for Phoenix Imaging Consultants, an interim and change management firm in Orlando, FL. Mr Lewis is also a partner in the firm of Imaging Fusion, a comprehensive medical imaging management firm in Hawthorne, NJ. His career spans 20 years of experience in medical imaging with work in both the inpatient and outpatient settings and he has been an active member of the AHRA since 1998. He has served in numerous capacities within the organization, including the Annual Meeting Design Team (chair in 2003), the 2001 Spring Conference Design Team, Membership Retention Task Force, Management Transition and Search Committees, and Policy and Procedures and By-Laws Committee. He is also teaching part of the CRA prep course in 2008. Mr Lewis was one of the inaugural CRAs, passing the exam in 2002, and is currently serving his second term on the AHRA Board of Directors. He served on the Finance Committee from 2004–2006 and is a member of the Imaging Advisory Council. In addition, Mr Lewis is a frequent speaker at AHRA meetings and has contributed to *Link* and *Radiology Management*. He is presently completing graduate studies in business administration.

Stephen Spearing, CRA, RT(R)
Imaging Services Director
Lewistown Hospital
Lewistown, Pennsylvania

Editor/Writer

J. Lynne Dodson
Creative Lines
Stratford, Connecticut

J. Lynne Dodson, a medical writer and editor since 1971, specializes in practice management, healthcare administration, patient education, and medical history. She is the author/co-author of 7 health-related books for general audiences, most recently, *Hot Times*, ghostwritten for bestselling nutritionist Ann Louise Gittleman, PhD. Ms Dodson is also the author of 5 photographic histories of medicine and a contributing author to the *Journal of Oncology Practice*. She has twice won writing excellence awards from the American Medical Writers Association. Through her Stratford, CT based business, Creative Lines, she also provides public relations services to nonprofit organizations.

Contributors

Stephen R. Gaines, MS, RT(R)(CT), CRA, CHE
District Administrative Director
Harris County Hospital District
Houston, Texas
Stephen Gaines is a Certified Radiology Administrator (CRA) and a Certified Healthcare Executive (CHE). He has held radiology leadership roles at Vanderbilt University Medical Center in Nashville, TN and the University of Texas Medical Branch in Galveston, TX. He is currently serving as the system-wide administrative director at the fourth largest public health system in the nation, Harris County Hospital District in Houston, TX and is also the principal consultant at Gaines Imaging Consultants specializing in business development and turnarounds. He holds master's degrees in healthcare administration and business.

Roberta M. Edge, MHA, CRA, FAHRA
Director of Imaging Services
Sutter Gould Medical Foundation
Modesto, California
Roberta "Robbie" Edge is the director of imaging services for Sutter Gould Medical Foundation in Modesto, CA. She has been working in imaging for 33 years, 21 of those in various management and leadership roles. Ms Edge has been actively involved with AHRA since 1994, volunteering in many capacities such as leading the Annual Meeting Design Team, serving on the Editorial Review Board, serving as education director on the Board of Directors, serving as president in 2004–2005, writing, and speaking. She was the Gold Awardee in 2006 and achieved Fellow status in 2000. Ms Edge was among the inaugural CRAs and holds a master's degree in health administration from Chapman University, a baccalaureate degree in general psychology from California State University, Northridge, and a radiology certificate from Lankenau Hospital in Philadelphia, PA.

Winnie Grieshaber, CRA, RT(R)(MR)
Retired, Director Medical Imaging
Shelbyville, Tennessee
Winnie Grieshaber worked for over 30 years in the imaging industry, more than 12 of those in management, and is now retired. She has been a member of AHRA

since 1999. Ms Grieshaber serves on the Editorial Review Board for *Radiology Management*, AHRA's peer reviewed journal, and volunteers with the Silent Auction at AHRA's annual meeting.

Becky Lamberth, MS, RT(R)(MR)
Director of Radiology/Radiation Safety Officer
Plaza Medical Center of Fort Worth
Fort Worth, Texas

Becky Lamberth has 18 years of healthcare experience in a variety of positions in both hospital and outpatient environments. Ms Lamberth completed her bachelor of science and a master of science in healthcare administration from Midwestern State University. She is a member of AHRA and has participated on the Annual Meeting Design Team. She has published and presented for AHRA, as well as lectured at several local society meetings and universities. Ms Lamberth is currently pursuing her MBA from the University of Texas at Arlington.

Debra A. Lopez, BS, RT(R), CRA, FAHRA
Director Diagnostic Imaging
Santa Clara Valley Medical Center
San Jose, California

Deb Lopez is the director of imaging services at Santa Clara Valley Medical Center in San Jose, CA. She has been working in the imaging field for 33 years, 21 years in her current position. Ms Lopez has been an AHRA member since 1988, received her CRA credential in 2002, and earned Fellow status in 2003. She chaired the AHRA Electronic Imaging Conference for 2 years and is currently serving a second term on the AHRA Board of Directors. She participated on the Novation Imaging council for several years, serving as chair and past-chair in 2003 and 2004, and also on the UHC Steering Committee. Ms Lopez has been a speaker at various AHRA meetings and currently teaches 2 AHRA Leadership Institute courses.

Peter C. McCormack, MHSA, RT(R), CRA
Associate Director
Scott & White
Temple, Texas

Peter C. McCormack is the associate director of radiology at Scott & White, the primary teaching and research hospital for Texas A&M Health Science Center College of Medicine. Mr McCormack obtained a bachelor of science degree in radiologic sciences from the University of Central Florida, Orlando and a master of science degree in health services administration at Nova Southeastern University, Ft. Lauderdale, FL. He has over 24 years in radiology management in both group practice and hospital settings. Mr McCormack is an active member of AHRA and the Association of Academic Administrators in Radiology and holds the CRA credential.

Kathy Tabor McEwan, ALB, RT(R)
Executive Director of Imaging
Boca Raton Community Hospital
Boca Raton, Florida

Kathy Tabor McEwan held various management and leadership positions at Massachusetts General Hospital in Boston, MA, prior to becoming the Executive Director of Imaging at Boca Raton Community Hospital. Her technical background includes work in MRI, CT, interventional, radiation therapy planning, emergency radiology, and contrast media research. She has consulted nationally and internationally, published a variety of articles and abstracts, and has been a guest lecturer at national and international conferences such as the Netherlands National Symposium, Radiologic Society of North America, and the American Society of Healthcare Administrators. She is a senior consultant with RCG Healthcare and has significant experience in workflow management, project planning, and tactical project implementation. She holds a bachelor's degree from Harvard University in Cambridge, MA.

Martha Munhall
Human Resources Generalist
Massachusetts General Hospital
Boston, Massachusetts

Martha Munhall holds a BA in English and a BA in history. She has spent the past 7 years as human resources generalist for the department of radiology at Massachusetts General Hospital (MGH). Prior to MGH, she spent 5 years working as a regional employee relations and recruitment manager for a national pharmacy chain.

Thomas A. Redman, MBA, CRA, FAHRA
Director of Radiology
Inova Fairfax Hospital
Falls Church, Virginia

Tom Redman is the director of radiology services for Inova Fairfax Hospital in Falls Church, VA. He has over 26 years of experience in the field of imaging, with 20 years in radiology management. Mr Redman has been actively involved with AHRA since 1994. He has served on a number of committees, including chair of the RACC, and achieved Fellow status in 2007. He holds a master's degree in business and a baccalaureate degree in radiation science from Virginia Commonwealth University in Richmond. Mr Redmond received his radiographer training from the University of Virginia Medical Center in Charlottesville, VA.

Gigi Vanacore
Radiology Manager
H. Lee Moffitt Cancer Center & Research Institute
Tampa, Florida

Gigi Vanacore is the director of radiology operations at the H. Lee Moffitt Cancer Center, a world renowned cancer hospital and one of the Designated National Cancer Institutes. She has been working at Moffitt for over 20 years. Ms Vanacore has been responsible for the management and support of multiple departments which include diagnostic radiology, CT, nuclear medicine, PET/CT, ultrasound, interventional radiology, angiography, MRI, PACS, radiology IT, radiology nursing, and all support services, including quality assurance and radiology research. She is happily married, has 2 girls, and is very proud of the challenging and changing field of radiology and its professionals.

Ed Yoder, RT(R), MHA
Administrative Director of Medical Imaging
Medical Imaging Department
Winter Haven Hospital
Winter Haven, Florida

Ed Yoder has more than 15 years of varied imaging management experience. He received his associate of applied science degree in radiology while completing his radiology training at the Cleveland Clinic. He went on to obtain a bachelor of arts degree in psychology from Baldwin-Wallace College in Berea, OH and then his master of hospital administration degree at St Francis University in Joliet, IL. He is an active member of the AHRA and is on the AHRA Board of Directors, the Editorial Review Board, and the AHRA Webinar Design Team. He has written many articles for *Radiology Management* and has authored chapters in other AHRA books. Mr Yoder is also involved with the Healthcare Financial Management Association and the American Society of Radiologic Technologists.

Reviewers

Sandy Anderson, MSHA, CRA
Director, OP Radiology & Imaging
Services
Memorial Health System
Colorado Springs, Colorado

Michael Brokloff
Vice President, Service
DMS Health Group
Fargo, North Dakota

Barbara Corigliano
Director of Imaging
Crystal Run Healthcare
Rock Hill, New York

Paul Dubiel
Director of Imaging Services
Seton Family of Hospitals
Austin, Texas

Debi Farnham, ARRT, CRT
Manager of Medical Imaging
Enloe Medical Center
Chico, California

David R. Fox, MBA, CRA
Director of Radiology
Baptist Health
Little Rock, Arkansas

Carolyn Groover
HR Director
Winter Haven Hospital
Winter Haven, Florida

Hazel Hacker, FAHRA
Business Manager
Edison Imaging Associates P.A.
Edison, New Jersey

**Robin Kirschner, RN, EdDc,
CRN, CPAN**
Senior Clinical Manager, Medical Imaging
Banner Desert Medical Center
Higley, Arizona

Larry T. Leopold
Manager of Radiology
Wichita Clinic PA
Wichita, Kansas

Stephanie Miller
Executive Director of Human Resources
Sutter Gould Medical Foundation
Modesto, California

Marcia Mortensson, SPHR, CEBS
HR Consultant
Sacramento, California

Tom Saladino, MPS, CRA
Faculty
Institute for Healthcare Communication
Lake Worth, Florida

**Wayne Stockburger, JD, MBA, RT(R),
FAHRA, FACHE**
Assistant Executive Director
Scott and White Health Systems
Temple, Texas

James W. Sutton, CRA, FAHRA, RT
Radiology Director
Fairmont Medical Center/Mayo Health
System
Fairmont, Minnesota

Jason Theadore, CRA, BS, RT(R)
Director of Medical Imaging
OhioHealth Neighborhood Care
Columbis, Ohio

Carlos Vasquez, MS, CRA
Division Director, Radiology Services
St. Elizabeth Regional Health
Lafayette, Indiana

Mark Watts, BS, RTR, CRA
System Manager, Imaging
Provena Health
Joliet, Illinois

Michele West
Director of Human Resources
Doctors Medical Center
Modesto, California

1

Human Resource Planning

In this section:

Chapter 1

The Impact of Employment Law on Human Resource Practices

Thomas A. Redman

Understanding employment law is a challenging but necessary subject for all managers. Employment law covers the complex aspects of the worker-employer relationship in all phases of the employment experience. No matter how many employees work in an organization, managers must know about the anti-discrimination laws and workplace safety regulations that govern employment practices. There are a number of federal and individual state laws covering the employment relationship that an organization must comply with. These laws are designed to require that all individuals be given equal opportunity and protection in employment.

Understanding these obligations reduces the occurrence of unlawful employment practices, which can lead to liability and unnecessary financial outlays. Proactive organizations minimize potential legal problems by understanding the laws and taking steps to reduce liability. Although this chapter provides a comprehensive overview of the current laws, this material does not constitute legal advice.

Laws Prohibiting Discriminatory Practices

There are a number of key federal laws that prohibit employment discrimination enforced by the Equal Employment Opportunity Commission (EEOC). The EEOC provides coordination and oversight of all federal equal employment opportunity laws and policies.

The EEOC is an independent federal agency that was created by Congress in 1964. The EEOC has 5 commissioners and a general counsel appointed by the president and confirmed by the Senate. The president designates a chair and a vice chair; the chair is the chief executive officer of the commission. The 5-member commission makes equal employment opportunity policy and approves most litigation.

The general counsel is responsible for conducting EEOC enforcement litigation under Title VII of the Civil Rights Act of 1964, the Equal Pay Act, the Age Discrimination in Employment Act, and the Americans with Disabilities Act. In addition to enforcement, the EEOC also provides education and technical assistance through 50 offices located throughout the nation.

Refer to Sidebar 1.1 for the major anti-discrimination laws.

Under Title VII of the Civil Rights Act of 1964, the Americans with Disabilities Act, and the Age Discrimination in Employment Act, it is illegal to discriminate in any aspect of employment, including the following[1]:

- Hiring, performance evaluations, and promotions
- Discipline and discharge
- Compensation, work assignments, or classification of employees
- Transfer, promotion, layoff, or recall
- Job advertisements
- Recruitment
- Testing
- Use of company facilities
- Training and apprenticeship programs
- Fringe benefits
- Pay, retirement plans, and disability leave

Title VII generally applies to employers with 15 or more employees, including state and local governments. It also applies to employment agencies and to labor organizations, as well as to the federal government. Employers are required to post notices to all employees advising them of their rights under the laws enforced by the EEOC and their right to be free from retaliation.[1]

SIDEBAR 1.1: Major Anti-Discrimination Laws

- Title VII of the Civil Rights Act of 1964
- Equal Pay Act of 1963
- Age Discrimination in Employment Act of 1967
- Rehabilitation Act of 1973, Sections 501 and 505
- Titles I and V of the Americans with Disabilities Act of 1990
- Civil Rights Act of 1991

An employer may not fire, demote, harass, or otherwise retaliate against an individual for filing a charge of discrimination, participating in a discrimination proceeding, or otherwise opposing discrimination. Employees have a right to be free from retaliation for their opposition to discrimination or their participation in an EEOC proceeding by filing a charge, testifying, assisting, or otherwise participating in an agency proceeding.

In addition to the protections against retaliation that are included in all of the laws enforced by the EEOC, the Americans with Disabilities Act also protects individuals from coercion, intimidation, threat, harassment, or interference in their exercise of their own rights or their encouragement of someone else's exercise of rights granted by the Americans with Disabilities Act.

Title VII of the Civil Rights Act of 1964

Title VII of the Civil Rights Act of 1964, as ammended by the Equal Employment Opportunity Act of 1972, prohibits employment discrimination based on race, color, religion, sex, and national origin. An exception to prohibited employment practices may be permitted when religion, sex, or national origin is a bona fide occupational qualification necessary to the operation of a particular business or enterprise. The Civil Rights Act also exempts hospitals operated by religious corporations or societies, but only with respect to employees directly concerned with religious activities. Almost all employment in hospitals operated by religious bodies is unrelated to religious activity.[2] It prohibits employers from discriminating against individuals because of their religion in hiring, firing, and other terms and conditions of employment. Under Title VII, employers may not treat employees or applicants more or less favorably because of their religious beliefs or practices. Employees cannot be forced to participate in a religious activity as a condition of employment. An employer is required to reasonably accommodate the religious belief of an employee or prospective employee, unless doing so would impose an undue hardship. It is also unlawful to retaliate against an individual for opposing employment practices that discriminate based on religion or for filing a discrimination charge, testifying, or participating in any way in an investigation, proceeding, or litigation under Title VII.

Equal employment opportunity cannot be denied any person because of an individual's racial group, racial characteristics (eg, hair texture, color, facial features), or because of a marriage to or association with someone of a particular race or color. Job requirements must be uniformly and consistently applied to persons of all races and colors. Even if a job requirement is applied consistently, if it is not important for job performance or business needs, the requirement may be found unlawful if it excludes persons of a certain racial group or color significantly more than others.

Title VII prohibits offensive conduct, such as racial or ethnic slurs, racial "jokes," derogatory comments, or other verbal or physical conduct based on an individual's race or color. Employers are required to take appropriate steps to prevent and correct unlawful harassment. Likewise, employees are responsible for reporting harassment at an early stage to prevent its escalation. Further, Title VII is violated when employees who belong to a protected group are segregated by physical isolation from other employees or from customer contact. In addition, employers may not assign employees according to race or color.

It is unlawful to discriminate against any employee or applicant for employment because of the individual's sex. This law prohibits employment decisions based on stereotypes and assumptions about abilities, traits, or the performance of individuals on the basis of sex. However, sexual orientation is not federally protected. Title VII prohibits both intentional discrimination and neutral job policies that disproportionately exclude individuals on the basis of sex and that are not job related. Title VII also prohibits compensation discrimination on the basis of sex. Unlike the Equal Pay Act, however, Title VII does not require that the employee's job be substantially equal to that of a higher paid person of the opposite sex or require the employee to work in the same establishment.

Sexual harassment is a form of sex discrimination that violates Title VII. Unwelcome sexual advances, requests for sexual favors, and other verbal or physical conduct of a sexual nature constitute sexual harassment when this conduct explicitly or implicitly affects an individual's employment, unreasonably interferes with an individual's work performance, or creates an intimidating or hostile work environment. Sexual harassment includes practices ranging from direct requests for sexual favors to workplace conditions that create a hostile environment for persons of either sex, including same-sex harassment. The term *quid pro quo* is used when harassment involves a promise in exchange for sexual favors or threat of rejection.[1] Only supervisors can commit this type of harassment. The hostile environment standard also applies to harassment on the bases of race, color, national origin, religion, age, and disability.

Sexual harassment can occur in a variety of circumstances. The harasser can be the victim's supervisor, an agent of the employer, a supervisor in another area, a co-worker, or a non-employee. The victim does not have to be the person harassed but could be anyone affected by the offensive conduct. The harasser's conduct must be unwelcome. When investigating allegations of sexual harassment, the EEOC looks at the entire record including the nature of the sexual advances and the context in which the alleged incidents occurred. A determination on the allegations is made from the facts on a case-by-case basis. From an employer's viewpoint, prevention is the best tool to eliminate sexual harassment in the workplace.

Title VII was amended by the Pregnancy Discrimination Act. Discrimination on the basis of pregnancy, childbirth, or related medical conditions constitutes unlawful sex discrimination. Women who are pregnant or affected by related conditions must be treated in the same way as other applicants or employees with similar abilities or with temporary illnesses or conditions.

Title VII's pregnancy-related protections include the following[1]:

- An employer cannot refuse to hire a pregnant woman because of her pregnancy or because of the prejudices of coworkers, clients, or customers.
- Pregnant employees must be permitted to work as long as they are able to perform their jobs.
- Employers must hold open a job for a pregnancy-related absence for the same length of time jobs are held open for employees on sick or disability leave (see section on Family and Medical Leave Act).
- Any health insurance provided by an employer must cover expenses for pregnancy-related conditions.
- Pregnancy-related benefits cannot be limited to married employees.
- Employees must be treated the same as other temporarily disabled employees for accrual and crediting of seniority, vacation calculation, pay increases, and temporary disability benefits.

Title VII also makes it unlawful to discriminate based on national origin. It is illegal to discriminate against an individual because of birthplace, ancestry, culture, linguistic characteristics common to a specific ethnic group, or marriage or other association with someone of a particular nationality. Rules such as requiring that employees speak only English on the job may violate Title VII unless an employer shows that the requirement is necessary for conducting business. In addition, the law prohibits discrimination against individuals employed in the United States, regardless of citizenship. However, relief may be limited if an individual does not have work authorization.

Equal Pay Act of 1963

The Equal Pay Act of 1963 prohibits discrimination on the basis of sex in the payment of wages or benefits, where men and women perform work of similar skill, effort, and responsibility for the same employer under similar working conditions. The Equal Pay Act requires that men and women be given equal pay for equal work in the same establishment. The jobs need not be identical, but they must be substantially equal. It is job content, not job title, that determines whether jobs are substantially equal.

Employers may not pay unequal wages to men and women who perform jobs that require substantially equal skill, effort, and responsibility and that are performed under similar working conditions within the same establishment. Each of these factors is summarized below[1]:

- Skill is measured by factors such as the experience, ability, education, and training required to perform the job. The key issue is what skills are required for the job, not what skills the individual employees may have.
- Effort is the amount of physical or mental exertion needed to perform the job.
- Responsibility is the degree of accountability required in performing the job.
- Working conditions include the physical surroundings like temperature, fumes, ventilation, and any hazards.
- Establishment refers to a distinct physical place of business rather than an entire business or enterprise consisting of several places of business. However, in some circumstances, physically separate places of business should be treated as one establishment.

Pay differentials are permitted when they are based on seniority, merit, quantity or quality of production, or a factor other than sex. The Equal Pay Act covers all employers who are covered by the Federal Wage and Hour Law (the Fair Labor Standards Act). Virtually all employers are subject to the provisions of this act.

Age Discrimination in Employment Act of 1967

The Age Discrimination in Employment Act of 1967 protects individuals who are 40 years of age or older from employment discrimination based on age. This act's age protections apply to both employees and job applicants. Under the Age Discrimination in Employment Act, it is unlawful to discriminate against a person because of his or her age with respect to any term, condition, or privilege of employment, including hiring, firing, promotion, layoff, compensation, benefits, job assignments, and training. The purpose of this law is to promote employment of older persons on the basis of their ability without regard to their age.[2]

The Age Discrimination in Employment Act's broad ban against age discrimination also specifically prohibits the following[1]:

- Statements or specifications in job notices or advertisements of age preference and limitations. An age limit may only be specified in the rare circumstance where age has been proven to be a *bona fide* occupational qualification.

- Discrimination on the basis of age by apprenticeship programs, including joint labor management apprenticeship programs.
- Denial of benefits to older employees. An employer may reduce benefits based on age only if the cost of providing the reduced benefits to older workers is the same as the cost of providing benefits to younger workers.

The Age Discrimination in Employment Act applies to private employers with 20 or more employees, including state and local governments. It also applies to employment agencies and most labor unions.[2]

Rehabilitation Act of 1973, Sections 501 and 505

The Rehabilitation Act of 1973, Sections 501 and 505, prohibits discrimination against individuals with disabilities who work in the federal government. Section 501 prohibits employment discrimination against individuals with disabilities in the federal sector. It requires federal agencies to establish affirmative action plans for the hiring, placement, and advancement of people with disabilities in federal employment. It mandates federal employers to make reasonable accommodations for disabilities related to their employee's job duties and performance.

Section 505 contains provisions governing remedies and attorney's fees under Section 501. Section 505 establishes the enforcement procedures for Title V of the Rehabilitation Act.

Americans with Disabilities Act

Titles I and V of the Americans with Disabilities Act of 1990 prohibit employment discrimination against qualified individuals with disabilities in job application procedures, hiring, firing, advancement, compensation, job training, and other conditions of employment. This act applies to the private sector, in state and local governments, employment agencies, and labor unions. This act's nondiscrimination standards also apply to federal sector employees under section 501 of the Rehabilitation Act. An individual with a disability is a person who has a physical or mental impairment that substantially limits one or more major life activities, has a record of such an impairment, or is regarded as having such an impairment.

A qualified employee or applicant with a disability is someone who satisfies skill, experience, education, and other job-related requirements of the position held or desired, and who, with or without reasonable accommodation, can perform the essential functions of that position.

An employer is required to make a reasonable accommodation to the known disability of a qualified applicant or employee if it would not impose an "undue hardship" on the operation of the employer's business. Undue hardship is defined as an action requiring significant difficulty or expense when considering such factors as an employer's size, financial resources, and nature of its operation.

An employer is not required to lower quality or production standards to make an accommodation, nor is an employer obligated to provide personal use items such as eye glasses or hearing aids.

Title I of the Americans with Disabilities Act covers medical examinations and inquiries. Employers may not ask job applicants about the existence, nature, or severity of a disability. Applicants may be asked about their ability to perform specific job functions. A job offer may be conditioned on the results of a medical examination, but only if the examination is required for all entering employees in similar jobs. Medical examinations of employees must be job related and consistent with the employer's business needs.

Title I also addresses drug and alcohol abuse.[3] Employees and applicants currently engaging in the illegal use of drugs are not covered. Tests for illegal drugs are not subject to the Americans with Disabilities Act's restrictions on medical examinations. Employers may hold illegal drug users and alcoholics to the same performance standards as other employees.

The Civil Rights Act of 1991

The Civil Rights Act of 1991 made major changes in the federal laws against employment discrimination enforced by the EEOC. Enacted in part to reverse several Supreme Court decisions that limited the rights of persons protected by these laws, this act also provides additional protections. The Civil Rights Act authorizes compensatory and punitive damages in cases of intentional discrimination, and provides for obtaining attorneys' fees and the possibility of trial by jury based on discrimination claims. It introduced the possibility of emotional distress damages, while limiting the amount that a jury could award. The Civil Rights Act also directs the EEOC to expand its technical assistance and outreach activities.

Companies based in the United States that employ American citizens outside the United States or its territories, and multinational employers that operate in the United States or its territories, are covered under equal employment opportunity laws, with some exceptions.

Family and Medical Leave Act

The Family and Medical Leave Act (FMLA) of 1993 obligates certain employers to provide family and temporary medical leave to their employees. The purpose of this act is to assist employees with family demands while remaining employed. It was enacted as a means of balancing the demands of the workplace with the needs of families, and promoting the stability, integrity, and economic security of families in a manner that accommodates the legitimate interests of employers.

FMLA is a federal labor law that provides unpaid, job protected leave to eligible employees, both male and female, in order to care for their families or themselves for specified family and medical conditions. This act covers private sector employers with 50 or more employees within 75 miles of the work site. Part time employees are counted toward the 50 employee minimum. This act also applies to all US government employees and state employees.[4]

Covered employers must grant an eligible employee up to a total of 12 work weeks of unpaid leave during any 12 month period for one or more of the following reasons[1]:

- For the birth and care of the newborn child of the employee
- For placement with the employee of a son or daughter for adoption or foster care
- To care for an immediate family member (spouse, child, or parent) with a serious health condition
- To take medical leave when the employee is unable to work because of a serious health condition

In general, FMLA ensures that all workers are able to take extended leaves of absence from work to handle family issues or illness without fear of being terminated from their jobs by their employers or being forced into a lower job upon their return. To be eligible, an employee must have worked for the employer at least 12 months and at least 1250 hours within a 12 month period before the leave begins.

Under certain conditions, an employee may use the 12 weeks of leave intermittently. An employee may elect to substitute annual leave and/or sick leave, consistent with current laws. Upon return from leave, an employee must be returned to the same position or to an "equivalent position with equivalent benefits, pay, status, and other terms and conditions of employment."[4]

Under FMLA, an employer may request medical certification for leave taken to care for an employee's spouse, child, or parent who has a serious health condition or for the serious health condition of the employee. A "serious health condition" under this act includes illness, injury impairment, or a physical or mental condition that involves inpatient care (defined as an overnight stay in a medical facility) and any related incapacity, and continuing treatment by a healthcare provider. An employer may require a medical certification that gives medical facts confirming the type of serious health condition. If the certification is for the employee's own serious health condition, it may require information on the employee's inability to perform essential job functions. An employer may require additional medical opinions at the employer's expense. Under FMLA, an employee with a serious health condition qualifies for leave when he or she is unable to perform any one of his or her essential job functions or must be absent in order to receive medical treatment for that condition.

This act prohibits an employer from discouraging, preventing, or retaliating against an employee seeking or using leave, and prohibits an employer from discriminating against or discharging an employee for leave-related matters. The US Department of Labor is authorized to investigate and resolve complaints of violations of this act, and an eligible employee may bring a civil action against an employer for violations.

FMLA does not affect any federal or state law prohibiting discrimination, or supersede any state or local law or collective bargaining agreement that provides greater family or medical leave rights. If other federal and state laws or a union contract provides greater benefits than FMLA, the employer is obligated to provide the greater benefits and explain any different requirements.

Occupational Safety and Health Act

The Occupational Safety and Health Act was initially created by Congress in 1970. Its purpose is to prevent work-related illnesses, injuries, and deaths by issuing and enforcing health and safety standards in the workplace.

Under this act, the Occupational Safety and Health Administration (OSHA) was created. It is an agency of the Department of Labor. Its primary mission is to ensure the safety and health of US workers by setting and enforcing standards and encouraging continual improvement in safety and health in the workplace. Employees or their representatives have the right to file complaints with an OSHA office and request a survey when they believe that conditions in the workplace are unsafe or unhealthy. If a violation of this act is found at the time of a survey, the employer may receive a citation stating a timeframe within which the violation must be corrected. Nearly every worker in the country comes under OSHA's jurisdiction except for miners, transportation workers, many public employees, and the self-employed.[5]

An employer can be held legally liable for damages suffered by employees through exposure to dangerous conditions that are in violation of OSHA standards.[2] The act provides penalties, including criminal negligence, when a standard violation results in a worker's death.

Since this act was approved, there have been a number of significant initiatives. During the Carter administration, OSHA concentrated on health hazards such as toxic chemicals. During the Reagan presidential years, new rules were issued. One was the right to know about chemical exposures by enacting new standards for hazardous communications. Another change was improved standards for blood-borne pathogens.

This same act also created the National Institute for Occupational Safety and Health.[6] This research agency determines the types of major hazards in the workplace and how to control them.

The Immigration Reform and Control Act

The Immigration and Nationality Act of 1952 established the framework of US immigration laws. Since 1952, there have been several public laws amending the Immigration and Nationality Act. One such law is the Immigration Reform and Control Act (IRCA) of 1986.

Federal immigration law determines whether a person is an alien and the associated legal rights, duties, and obligations of aliens in the United States. It also provides means by which certain aliens can become naturalized citizens with full rights of citizenship. Immigration law also serves as a gatekeeper for the nation's border: it determines who may enter, how long they may stay, and when they must leave.

The IRCA is a law that was created with the intention to reduce illegal immigration to the United States. At the time, it was perceived as an economic problem for the US economy. There were a large number of immigrants in the United States during the 1980s who were either unemployed or illegal. The law criminalized the act of knowingly hiring an illegal immigrant. The law established financial and other penalties for those employing illegal aliens. It was perceived that not as many people would desire to enter the United States illegally if the prospects for employment were low.[7]

The IRCA makes it unlawful for an employer to hire any person who is not legally authorized to work in the United States, and it requires employers to verify the employment eligibility of all new employees. This includes permanent residents, temporary residents, refugees, and asylees. The law established a 1 year amnesty program for illegal aliens who had already worked and lived in the United States since January 1982. Those eligible could apply for regularization of status and eventually full citizenship. The law mandated the increased use of border patrol activities and the auditing of employer I-9 forms. Over 2.7 million illegal aliens and others not qualifying for visas were legalized under the 1986 IRCA amnesty.[7]

The IRCA also prohibits discrimination in hiring and discharge based on national origin (as does Title VII) and citizenship status. Its anti-discrimination provisions are intended to prevent employers from attempting to comply with the IRCA's work authorization requirements by discriminating against foreign looking or foreign sounding job applicants.

The IRCA corrected an unfair double standard in immigration law that prohibited unauthorized aliens from working in the United States but permitted employers to hire them. The IRCA of 1986 requires employers to ensure that employees hired are legally authorized to work in the United States. However, an employer who requests employment verification only for individuals of a particular national origin, or individuals who appear to be or sound foreign, may violate both Title VII and the IRCA. It is required that verification be obtained from all applicants and employees. Employers who impose citizenship requirements or give preferences to US citizens in hiring or employment opportunities also may violate the IRCA.

Employer sanction provisions of the IRCA include the following[8]:

- It makes it unlawful for any person knowingly to hire, recruit, or refer for a fee any alien not authorized to work, and establishes penalties for non-compliance.
- It requires employers to verify all newly hired employees by examining either a US passport, a US citizenship certificate, a certificate of naturalization, resident alien card, or a combination of papers showing identity and authority to work.
- It requires each employer to attest to documentation before any hiring.
- It requires the employee to attest that he or she is authorized to work in the US.
- It establishes civil and criminal penalties for hiring illegal aliens, with a 6 month education period, and a subsequent 12 month warning period.
- It requires employers, recruiters, and those who refer for employment to keep records.

The IRCA established the Office of Special Counsel for Immigration-Related Unfair Employment Practices to enforce the IRCA anti-discrimination provision.

This is managed under the US Department of Justice. The Special Counsel is to investigate and prosecute any charges of discrimination stemming from unlawful immigration-related employment practices.[8] It prohibits employers with at least 4 employees from discriminating against legal residents on the basis of citizenship.

The IRCA's national origin discrimination provisions apply to employers with between 4 and 14 employees who would not be covered by Title VII. Employers of 15 or more employees should note that the ban on national origin discrimination against any individual under Title VII of the Civil Rights Act of 1964 continues to apply. Employers can demonstrate compliance with the law by following the verification (I-9 form) requirements and treating all new hires the same. This includes establishing a policy of hiring only individuals who are authorized to work. A "US citizens only" policy in hiring is illegal. Employers must complete the I-9 form for all new hires and permit employees to present any document or combination of documents acceptable by law.

Conclusion

The scope of labor employment law is broad. When complex questions arise, legal counsel may be the best alternative. Laws must be followed in order for employee rights to be protected and preserved. If the organization is sued for violations, the costs can be staggering. Some organizations have been penalized with multimillion dollar verdicts.[9] Managers must be cognizant of the risks of litigation inherent in employment relationships. Managers have an obligation to minimize risks by taking lawful action while protecting business interests.

References

1. US Equal Employment Opportunity Commission. Available at: http://www.eeoc.gov. Accessed March 12, 2006.

2. Pozgar GD. *Legal Aspects of Health Care Administration*. 10th ed. Sudbury, MA: Jones & Bartlett Publishers; 2006.

3. Wendover RW. *Smart Hiring at the Next Level*. Naperville, IL: Sourcebooks, Inc.; 2006.

4. US Department of Labor. Available at: http://www.dol.gov. Accessed April 10, 2006.

5. US Department of Labor Occupational Safety & Health Administration. Available at: http://www.osha.gov. Accessed July 17, 2006.

6. Centers for Disease Control and Prevention. Avaliable at: http://www.cdc.gov/Niosh/about.html. Accessed August 2, 2006.

7. US Citizenship and Immigration Services. Available at: http://www.uscis.gov. Accessed May 25, 2006.

8. Legal Services Corporation Office of Inspector General. Available at: http://www.oig.lsc.gov. Accessed May 25, 2006.

9. Rosen LS. *The Safe Hiring Manual.* Tempe, AZ: Facts on Demand Press, 2004.

Chapter 2

Building a Workforce Plan

Steve Gaines

A critical component of a facility's strategic plan, a workforce (or staffing) plan is created by performing an analysis on workforce supply and demand, the gaps that are likely to occur between the current supply of workers and future needs, and possible solutions. With the aid of human resource information systems, industry benchmarks, and the facility's own personnel database, the imaging administrator can put together a plan to meet the facility's goals over a 3 to 5 year period.

A workforce, or staffing, plan is a key component of an organization's strategic plan. The strategic plan outlines what the organization and its environment will be like at some specified future time, frequently set at 3 to 5 years from the present. It also includes the tactical or operational plan that will enable the organization to envision the future. It has been described as analogous to a house plan. The strategic plan describes how many rooms the house will have, how large it will be, and what its configuration and primary building materials will be. The tactical plan describes how the house will be built and by whom.[1]

Workforce planning ensures that people strategies align with the organization's strategic plan. It is a framework that guides an assessment and analysis of the impact of internal and external trends on the workforce, considers the current state, explores alternate futures, and then highlights actions to define and create the preferred future workforce that is capable of delivering the organization's strategy.

Labor is the single largest expense incurred by any healthcare organization and one of the most critical elements in the organization's success. No strategic plan is complete without a description of the staff needed to carry it out. The primary function of the workforce plan is to accurately identify the required number of personnel possessing the necessary skill sets needed to "get the job done" at any given time. In other words, the workforce plan is a road map of how many people and the type of people it takes to work in the department so that it properly functions under different scenarios. In general, the workforce plan includes the following:

- Projected workforce level, categorized by department or major activity, skill levels, and employee group.
- Projected workforce changes (plus or minus) through retirement, recruitment, etc.
- Cost projections, including wages, benefits, and indirect costs (eg, additional workspace, computers).
- Any changes planned in employment policies or compensation (eg, use of temporary workers, likely outcome of union contract negotiations, addition of a new health benefit).

With the availability of human resource information systems, computers have taken on some of the tedious calculations and can even provide projections and "what if" scenarios for discussion and analysis. Nevertheless, preparing a detailed, useful workforce plan will take some time but will prove invaluable and time saving. Such a plan will guide timing of recruitment efforts; provide the basis for equipment, labor, and capital budgeting; and help develop training schedules. It may forestall the need for layoffs by enabling management to either overcome conditions that will likely lead to demand decline or take full advantage of projected attrition.

In all but the very smallest imaging facilities, preparing a workforce plan is a group effort, with participation by administrators or managers of all major units. When available, the facility's strategic plan serves as the starting point. If none has been developed, then the group may need to work from the mission statement or previous workforce plans, or create a strategic plan for the areas within its scope of responsibility.

No matter who creates the workforce plan, 4 categories of data need to be analyzed:

1. Supply: Who are the current staff?
2. Demand: What staff will be needed to carry out the strategic plan?
3. Gap: How does the projected supply fail to meet the projected demand?
4. Solutions: How will the facility resolve the gap issues?

Supply Analysis

Three types of information are essential to analyze the current supply of workers: workforce demographics, workforce competencies, and trends. Taken together, they provide a relatively accurate picture of current staff and a basis for eventual gap analysis.

Workforce Demographics

Who are the men and women who compose the facility's present day staff? Such a question is not mere idle curiosity. A predominantly young, female staff is likely to have a higher attrition rate and call for greater recruitment effort over the next 3 to 5 years than a middle aged team with substantial seniority.

The imaging facility's human resource information system should be able to provide file data for the following characteristics of all current employees (see also Sidebar 2.1):

SIDEBAR 2.1: The Diverse Face of the Workforce

Analyzing the demographics of a facility's workforce highlights the degree of diversity represented. Although commonly viewed as relating to ethnic and racial differences, largely as a result of employment legislation, workforce diversity is seen in a much broader context by many experts. For example, in the book *Managing the Mosaic*, Svehla and Crosier list 12 primary and secondary elements that contribute to workforce diversity[2]:

Primary (largely beyond the individual's control)

- Age
- Ethnicity
- Sex
- Physical abilities
- Race
- Sexual orientation

Secondary (within the individual's control to change)

- Educational background
- Geographic location
- Income
- Marital status
- Military experience
- Parental status

They point out that every employee brings his/her culture and values to the workplace, where ideally they effectively blend with the organization's culture and values. Managing such a diverse workforce calls for challenging assumptions, learning to recognize and overcome stereotypes and prejudices, and accepting that "differences are neither good nor bad; they are simply different."[2]

By incorporating measures of diversity into each of the 4 analytical stages of preparing a workforce plan, the imaging administrator should also have a plan that enables him/her to meet community and facility expectations for workforce diversity.

- Age
- Sex
- Race/national origin
- Length of service
- Retirement eligibility
- Job classification
- Pay grade

An administrator of an imaging facility that has a large staff and/or multiple divisions, such as diagnostic imaging and interventional cardiology, may want to create summary documents for each division, as well as for the entire facility. If, for example, the strategic plan calls for expanding 1 division, having 2 levels of data will make gap and solution analyses more accurate and meaningful.

Workforce Competencies

Competencies encompass skills, knowledge, abilities, and personal attributes that, taken together, are critical to successful work accomplishment.[3] An organization's core competencies are those that are most critical to its success; they help define who the organization is and what it does well. A second level of competency can be defined for each staff member and indicates the knowledge and skill the employee brings to his or her job. Congruence between organizational and individual competencies is characteristic of highly successful facilities.

Licensing and certification standards for some professionals (eg, imaging technologists) offer a starting point to identify competencies. A review of personnel records can also identify existing individual skills and knowledge. The US Department of Health and Human Services suggests studying how the top performing employees in each job category carry out their jobs.[3] Employee questionnaires, focus groups, and individual interviews with the employees and their managers are among the ways to collect data. These techniques can also be used to establish core competencies for the organization. Reviewing patient satisfaction surveys and conducting patient focus groups may provide insight into the nontechnical competencies (eg, ability to clearly communicate) of all staff, including patient access, registration, scheduling, billing, and administrative assistants. Identified competencies should also include those arising from an employee's diversity (eg, multilinguality).

Reviewing Trends

The data set produced from trend analysis spans past, present, and future as it reveals activities that bring about workforce turnover. Based on the facility's demographic data and computer analysis of past workforce changes, trend analysis examines

---

the impact of retirement, termination, resignation, long term disability, death, and transfer/promotion. For example, if a facility's current turnover rate is 35% per year and no effort is made to lower it, can the facility successfully carry out a plan to expand its diagnostic services? If a third of an organization's technologists reach retirement age during the next 5 years, what is the likely effect on the strategic plan?

Given the shortages of qualified imaging technologists in some regions of the United States, trend analysis should also examine the facility's vacancy rates and duration of recruitment efforts to fill a position. The impact of shortages affects employee morale and stress, as well as the ability of the facility to grow. Reviewing the average length of time to fill a position and the average vacancy rate for key positions over the past 5 years will reveal potential issues that will need to be specifically addressed during solution analysis.

Trend analysis should also incorporate a review of diversity trends within the staff and in the communities served by the facility. Data from the US Census Bureau, professional healthcare associations, and state and local government and chambers of commerce can be analyzed along with data generated by the facility's human resource information system for past and present workforce demographics. In particular, the administrator will want to examine changes that have taken place in the number and percentage of workers, patients, and local population by age, race, and ethnic origin.

For example, the US Census Bureau projects that by 2020, 14% of the population will be between 65 and 84 years of age, as Baby Boomers reach traditional retirement age and beyond.[4] This is likely to have a 3-fold impact on imaging services— fewer seasoned workers and radiologists available to staff facilities and greater demand for services by elderly patients. The bureau also projects that by 2050, Hispanics will compose 24% of the US population, whereas white non-Hispanics will be just 50% (down from 69% in 2000). In fact, all minorities will increase in proportion of population, as whites decline.[4] In some parts of the country, of course, ethnic and racial minorities already make up more than a quarter of the local population.

Data can be displayed as tables with ranges, mean, and median for age and race/ethnic origin over the past 5 to 10 years and projected for the next 5 to 10 years, for the workforce and for the community. A simple line graph that displays the mean internally and externally over the full time period can be an effective visual representation of how well the facility's workforce reflects its patient base and prepare for a solutions analysis.

Demand Analysis

Whereas supply analysis tends to be grounded in the present, demand analysis looks primarily to the future. As such, it relies on the facility's strategic plan, goals, and objectives for direction. The workforce demands for an imaging center that plans to merge with an interventional cardiology practice are considerably different from those of a hospital based radiology department that plans to convert to digital imaging.

One key to analyzing future workforce demand is to have an accurate measure of just how much work an employee (or full time equivalent [FTE], total annual hours worked = 2080) in a given job classification can perform in a specified period of time. One of the most commonly used tools for measuring workforce requirements is benchmarking data. A second measure, the relative value unit (RVU), is a more recent innovation most commonly used by the Medicare system to measure physician productivity, but is being adapted for use with other healthcare professionals.

Interpreting Benchmark Data

Several benchmarking products are available for purchase or acquisition through group memberships (eg, the Advisory Board Company, the American College of Radiology, University Health Consortium, and AHRA). Most group affiliations will have similar benchmarking data products relative to their industry focus.

The typical benchmarking tool will be a compilation of data collected through questionnaires acquired from like facilities. In most cases, the questionnaires ask about type and size of facility, examination volumes, workforce level per modality, and ancillary workforce levels. When the completed questionnaires are returned, the data are extracted, qualified, and compiled to reveal an overall average. The finalized and published data can then be used as a reference to determine a baseline for staffing at other similar facilities.

Benchmark data are excellent tools but should be understood in order to interpret and apply the results appropriately. Figure 2.1 presents an example, extracted from the 2006 edition of AHRA's *Staff Utilization Survey*.[5]

This particular data set represents the results of questions regarding the computed tomography (CT) average procedure volume per technologist FTE for all hospitals and non-hospitals. In other words, this figure demonstrates the volume of procedures an individual CT technologist performs on average in different types of environments. The data are segregated into types of facilities (eg, academic, pediatric,

Staffing

Average Procedure Volume per Technologist FTE in Computed Tomography

	n	Average	25th Percentile	Median	75th Percentile
All respondents	195	3,365	1,922	2,750	3,667
Organization type					
Hospital	148	3,463	1,978	2,750	3,614
200 or less	66	2,667	1,355	2,417	3,282
More than 200	81	4,090	2,304	2,763	3,877
Academic	30	3,689	2,400	3,264	4,167
Pediatric	1	.	.	.	.
Long term care	1	.	.	.	.
Community	116	3,444	1,878	2,605	3,435
Rehabilitation	0	.	.	.	.
Non Hospital	47	3,057	1,350	2,987	3,699
Imaging center	40	3,195	1,408	2,997	3,683
Multi-specialty physician office	4	.	.	.	.
Primary care clinic	2	.	.	.	.
Radiologist practice	0	.	.	.	.
Mobile service	1	.	.	.	.
Level 1 trauma center					
Yes	23	3,289	2,304	3,389	4,000
No	126	3,507	1,922	2,631	3,600
Do you have radiology residents training at your facility?					
Yes	30	3,400	2,304	3,005	3,980
No	120	3,492	1,939	2,606	3,600
Region					
Midwest	34	4,733	1,929	2,606	3,000
North Atlantic	42	3,325	2,250	3,437	4,167
Southwest	23	3,227	1,700	3,000	3,500
South	54	2,883	2,029	2,653	3,250
West	40	3,073	1,683	2,698	3,593
Procedure volume					
5,000 or less	56	1,956	1,049	1,499	2,755
5,001 - 10,000	36	2,975	1,956	2,819	3,583
10,001 - 20,000	52	3,316	2,253	2,750	3,593
20,001 or more	54	5,163	2,762	3,435	4,271
PACS					
No PACS	14	2,680	1,182	3,001	3,750
New PACS	83	2,848	1,757	2,332	3,360
Established PACS	89	4,040	2,400	2,993	3,980

ahra   Kerr & Downs Research

Figure 2.1 Sample Benchmarking Data for Staff Utilization.

Source: 2006 Staff Utilization Survey. Sudbury, MA: AHRA; 2006.

long term care, community, and rehabilitation) and further segregated into trauma centers, bed size, geographic regions, procedure volume, and those with and without picture archiving and communication systems (PACS).

An examination of the data reveals, for example, that there were 30 responses to the questionnaire from academic hospitals and the average CT volume per technologist was 3689 procedures per year. The imaging administrator could use this number as a baseline or could break it down further to compare to hospitals of similar size, geographic region, and so on. For example, an administrator of an imaging department in a 500 bed academic hospital in the South could scan the average column and find the average procedure volume per technologist of an academic hospital is 3689; the average for a 500 bed hospital is 4090; and the average in the South is 2883. There is a considerable range of 301 procedures between the results for an academic hospital and a 500 bed hospital. For benchmarking, the accuracy of these widely divergent averages would be improved by averaging the sum of the 3 results, which would be roughly 3554 CT procedures per technologist. A department that planned to install a new CT device and increase its CT procedure volume by 7000 within the next 12 months would need to plan for the addition of 2 FTEs to its workforce.

As with any averaged data, these benchmark data do not take into account individual circumstances that may affect worker productivity now or in the future. For example, facilities with established PACS consistently performed more procedures than those with newly installed systems, no doubt at least in part a result of the learning curve for new technology. The difference between the average productivity of those in the 25th percentile and those in the 75th percentile was usually significant (eg, in the Southwest, workers in the 75th percentile performed twice as many procedures as those in the 25th percentile).

Relative Value Units: Another Way to Measure Productivity

Whereas benchmark data based on procedures have the advantage of simplicity in compiling and understanding, they leave much to be desired in terms of specificity and comparability. Although the data are generally broken into major modalities to avoid direct comparison between CT and conventional radiography, for example, it is nevertheless true that within a given modality, considerable variation exists in the time needed to carry out individual procedures. Magnetic resonance imaging (MRI) of the head will take less time than full body MRI, yet each counts as 1 procedure in benchmark calculations based on activity.

A second productivity measure system has been developed that takes into account various factors that influence productivity. The relative value system (RVS) was initially devised in 1989 under the sponsorship of the American College of Radiology following a congressional mandate to the US Health Care Financing Administration (HCFA) to develop a fee schedule for imaging services under Medicare.[6] The RVS was subsequently expanded to cover all outpatient physician services.

An RVS assigns a value to each procedure or service that is greater or less than the value of other procedures based on factors such as effort expended, time consumed, and risks taken. This value, referred to as the RVU, reflects both time and mental effort.[7] In other words, a chest radiograph might carry an RVU of 1.00, whereas an MRI RVU could be 8.50. As devised for Medicare payment, the RVS used the same RVU for each procedure throughout the country; the RVU contained professional and technical components; and the system applied a regionally specific conversion factor to translate the RVU into dollars as a base for a fee schedule. These RVUs, assigned to every American Medical Association *Current Procedural Terminology* (CPT) code, and the fee schedule are updated annually and are available from the Centers for Medicare and Medicaid Services (CMS, formerly HCFA).[8]

The technical portion of the RVUs used for Medicare payment can be used to measure non-physician productivity and estimate workforce demand, in which case the RVU does not need to be converted to dollars. The facility's chargemaster with its CPT° codes can be linked with the RVU spreadsheets from CMS through the financial information system to yield the total of RVUs per time period (month, year, etc). Dividing by time worked will give the ratios for RVUs per hour or per FTE.

Table 2.1 is an example of a tool that can be used to measure and chart productivity month by month. Each modality has its own benchmark for numbers of RVUs and examinations, so each should be listed and calculated separately. Specifically, Table 2.1 was developed for an angiography unit. The benchmark for number of examinations performed monthly was calculated by dividing the average annual

Table 2.1 Sample Productivity Table to Measure and Monitor Technologist Productivity by Comparing Work Output with 2 Different Benchmarks for an Angiography Unit

Shift	No. of Examinations	% of Examination Benchmark*	Technologist	RVUs	% of RVU Benchmark†	Average (%)
1	124	114	1	978	98	106
1	125	115	2	1266	127	121
1	98	90	3	922	92	91
1	76	70	4	609	61	66
1	34	31	5	289	29	30

RVU indicates relative value unit.

*Examination benchmark = 109.

†RVU benchmark = 1000.

procedure volume per technologist FTE (1308) from the AHRA survey[5] by 12, giving a benchmark of 109. The RVU benchmark is set at 1000. Both benchmarks set a baseline, meaning that in a month's time a technologist FTE can perform 109 examinations and/or 1000 RVUs. Technologist 1 performed 124 examinations, or 114% of the examination benchmark. These procedures equated to 978 RVUs, falling short of the RVU benchmark of 1000. Although the technologist performed 15 procedures above the benchmark, because of the relative simplicity of the examinations, the RVU rating did not reach the benchmark. On the other hand, technologist 2 had roughly the same examination count as technologist 1, but had a much higher RVU rating. Technologist 2 performed relatively more difficult examinations, translating into higher RVU ratings. Again, RVUs are a way of comparing examinations by weighting their value using work output, length of time to perform, and level of difficulty.

To achieve a more accurate picture of productivity, the imaging administrator may find averaging the examination benchmark percentage and the RVU benchmark percentage useful. In Table 2.1, technologist 1 achieved an average of 106% on the 2 benchmarks; technologist 2 had an average of 121%. Each produced more than 100% of the combined benchmarks, a fair share of the workload.

Of course, even with available benchmarks from external sources such as AHRA and CMS, no single productivity target fits all circumstances. Differences in physical layout, patient acuity, equipment availability, and workforce expertise make every facility unique. Use of the facility's own data on numbers of procedures performed, patients served, etc, accumulated over time, may provide a mechanism for "customizing" external benchmarks. However, as guides to aid in workforce planning and projections, existing benchmarks remain useful tools.

With data on productivity levels for each job category and a strategic plan that outlines future projects, goals, and objectives, including workforce diversity levels, the imaging administrator can estimate future workforce demands. Human resource information systems can produce graphs or tables delineating workforce needs for each project, by modality, or for the entire facility at a given point. It is probably useful to also program one or more "what if" scenarios to estimate workforce demands if environmental factors change (eg, pending legislation is passed) or projects are cancelled.

Gap Analysis

Ideally, a comparison of workforce supply and future workforce demand will include both quantitative and qualitative analysis. Human resource information systems, for example, can produce line graphs depicting the variance between supply and demand quarterly or annually for the length of the current strategic plan. This visual presentation allows management to quickly identify timeframes for peak recruitment activity.

However, for larger facilities especially, it is equally important to identify gaps by job classification or even specific competencies. The solutions for filling a significant gap in imaging technologist positions may be different from those used to fill multiple administrative positions. To meet diversity goals, variance should be calculated for current minority staffing versus projected needs. Again, if goals call for a higher percentage of minority representation in supervisory or management roles, variance graphs need to be devised based on job classification and minority status.

Gap analysis identifies not only situations in which workforce supply will not meet demand, but also when supply is projected to exceed demand. This provides advance notice of a situation that could result in layoffs and an opportunity to intervene to prevent this.

Solution Analysis

The final section of the workforce plan needs to provide feasible solutions to the identified inconsistencies between projected workforce supply and demand. Staffing is about more than recruitment, and flexibility in considering options is invaluable. It is a rare facility that can add new positions as often as its staff would like. The types of solutions include:

■ Retraining and cross-training existing staff (eg, to eliminate layoffs, avoid recruiting time and expense, and fill short term or small gaps in competencies).
■ Reorganizing workflow (eg, to smooth out peaks and valleys of demand or to transfer tasks from imaging technologists to technology aides or administrative staff).
■ Recruiting and hiring from a diverse population and from a variety of resources (see Sidebar 2.2).
■ Community outreach to recruit volunteers and interns, provide scholarships, and develop networks with potential resources.

Following are two scenarios that demonstrate how flexibility in considering workforce options helps resolve issues of supply versus demand.

SIDEBAR 2.2: All Types of Workers for All Types of Needs

If the solution to a workforce supply/demand gap is to hire new staff, today's employment market offers a range of alternatives:

Full time employees: These permanent staff work 35 to 40 hours per week on the payroll of a single employer who is responsible for not only wages or salary, but also Social Security, payroll taxes, and workers' compensation. Benefits such as vacation; sick leave; health, dental, and life insurance; and holidays are paid for, and office/work space, tools, and supplies are provided. Full time employees provide the core of experienced workers and will usually be relied on to cover normal workflow.

Part time employees: An important asset in many healthcare settings, these workers most often work 20 hours or less per week, but maintain a regular schedule and a regular set of duties. These staff members are the 0.5 in 2.5 FTEs. Generally, they will receive the same benefits and have similar costs associated as full time employees, but on a prorated basis.

Temporary (contract) employees: These workers only work when needed, which may include working 3 months to cover for an employee on maternity leave or 1 afternoon per week to handle data entry overflow. Projects requiring specialized skills and of a limited duration are often carried out by temporary workers. They are commonly hired through specialty workforce agencies, which are responsible for recruiting, interviewing, and verifying qualifications, as well as wages, payroll taxes, and any benefits. Although the cost per hour is higher when the employee is hired through an agency because of its fee, the overall short term cost is lower because of savings on taxes, benefits, and recruiting.

Independent contractors (outsourcing): These are essentially businesses (although they may employ only 1 person) that take on a specific project for a set fee. They include a wide range of professionals from graphic artists to accountants to physicians. They are responsible for paying their own taxes, setting their own work schedule, and providing their own equipment and supplies.

Scenario 1

An imaging center plans to add interventional radiology services within the next 18 months.

- Demand: 0.5 FTE interventional radiology technologist needed initially, with 1.5 FTEs projected by end of 12 months.
- Supply: 1 FTE has previous experience with the modalities, but none currently on staff is a specialist.
- Gap: Current staff can probably fill the initial demand, but at least 1 additional FTE will be needed within 12 months.

Possible solutions:

1. Offer cross-training to current staff and share position with general radiography services.
2. Contract with workforce agency or independent contractor for long term assignment (leased worker) until demand reaches predetermined procedure levels to warrant full time permanent employee.
3. Identify program that trains technologists specializing in interventional radiology, attend on campus recruiting events, offer scholarship to a student who commits to work for a prespecified period, and develop a relationship with the placement office, with the goal of hiring 1 FTE.
4. Offer experienced staff person tuition reimbursement for refresher courses and transfer to new position. If accepted, this leaves 1 FTE gap in other services that will have to be filled.

Scenario 2

As part of a hospital-wide initiative, the imaging department seeks to have its staff better reflect the increasing ethnic diversity of its patient population, especially Asian and Hispanic groups. It has set a goal to increase minority staff numbers by an average of 10% per year for the next 3 years.

- Supply: Current workforce demographics show 10 of 55 non-physician employees are Hispanic, Asian, or African American; at least 1 FTE is expected to retire within the next 3 years.
- Demand: At least 7 FTEs (6 new and 1 replacement for retiree) hired over the next 3 years are to be ethnic minorities.

Possible solutions:

1. Retention of a diverse workforce requires an environment in which all employees have opportunities for career development and can work together harmoniously. Conduct an employee survey to identify current perceptions about the department's environment and to identify possible deficiencies that could be met by diversity training by a consultant.
2. Network with leaders of minority communities and organizations. Engage in discussions that identify key cultural values and issues important to these communities and work together to ensure they are reflected in the workplace. Take part in health and job fairs within these communities.
3. Identify effective mechanisms for job advertisement placement to reach potential workers, such as ethnic language newspapers, church or social club bulletins, and local university organizations for minority students.

4. Offer scholarships to minority students to attend imaging technologist and other related specialty training in exchange for an agreement for employment.

Table 2.2 demonstrates a basic workforce plan for two units, administrative and diagnostic imaging, of a fictitious imaging center. The growth in clerical and technical positions results from the center's strategic plan to invest in new diagnostic equipment to expand services to their region.

The Workforce Plan as a Living Document

Once written, the workforce plan is not just filed away. Not only is it used as noted for budgeting and other administrative planning, but it must also be reviewed regularly (usually annually) and revised as necessary. Why is there a need to review and revise the plan on a regular basis? Conditions change over time. People change. Technologies change. Workforce requirements change. Communities change. All of these environmental changes can impact the function and needs of the department. The changes may require workforce adjustments that should be reflected in the workforce plan.

For example, digital imaging technology, including digital radiography and PACS, has made an enormous impact on the imaging field. A pre-digital environment workforce

Table 2.2 Three Year Workforce Plan in FTEs for an Imaging Center with Plans to Expand Diagnostic Imaging Services

Category	Current Supply	Projected Demand			Projected Attrition/Year	Projected Gap		
		Year 1	Year 2	Year 3		Year 1	Year 2	Year 3
Administration Administrative/ Supervisory	7.0	7.0	7.5	7.5	1.0	1.0	1.5	1.5
Exempt Nonmanagement	0.5	0.5	1.0	1.0	0	0	1.5	1.5
Technical	2.0	2.5	3.0	5.0	1.5	2.0	3.5	4.5
Clerical	18.5	19.0	19.0	22.0	5.0	5.5	5.5	8.5

Solutions: Contact local businesses and high schools; take part in job fairs; develop relationships with career counselors and placement officers; send speakers to health career classes. Provide training incentives for current staff to develop management potential. Use performance evaluation process to identify and mentor potential supervisory personnel.

Diagnostic Imaging Technical	35.0	35.0	36.0	40.0	7.0	7.0	8.0	12.0
RN	3.0	3.0	3.5	4.0	1.5	1.5	2.0	2.5

Solutions: Sponsor booth at national conference. Provide scholarship to student attending technologist training program in exchange for employment agreement. Recruit among ethnic communities to broaden scope of search. Offer signing and referral bonuses for technical positions.

plan most likely included a large workforce of film/file room clerks and darkroom technicians because all images were on hard copy film, which had to be processed, handled, and stored. However, in a digital environment where there is no hard copy image, the need for these positions has dwindled. Today, many facilities are completely digital and have reengineered the film and darkroom staff jobs to include a PACS administrator, PACS support, and image library staff. To remain productive, a pre-digital environment workforce plan for these facilities would need to be substantially revised.

In addition to major technologic changes, other events that can significantly affect workforce (and strategic) plans include the following: changes in competitive factors (a new imaging center opens nearby), changes in a major service (addition of a new diagnostic imaging unit), changes in government regulations (new licensing requirements), acquisition or merger, rapid growth (shift in patient demographics), or changes in senior management.

Conclusion

The field of radiology has seen dramatic developments in technology during its history, but one fundamental remains. Without humans to operate the equipment, assist patients, analyze the results, and carry out the myriad other procedures in a modern imaging facility, the technologic developments are worthless. Although all businesses need workforce plans to address their current and future personnel needs, most do not have to staff 365 days per year, 24 hours per day, 7 days per week, nor are their staff called on to deal with life threatening situations with little or no notice, as do those who work in at least certain types of imaging facilities. Strategic planning within diagnostic imaging services over the coming years will demand consideration of not only technologic capability and reimbursement economics, but also sustained focus on talent management and establishment of an efficient operational structure, to maintain quality patient care. As an integral part of the facility's strategic plan, a workforce plan ensures qualified personnel are always at work for their patients.

References

1. Tracey WR, ed. *Human Resources Management and Development Handbook.* New York, NY: American Management Association; 1985.

2. Svehla TA, Crosier GC. *Managing the Mosaic: Addressing Workforce Diversity and Managing Institutional Change in Health Care.* Chicago, IL: American Hospital Association; 1994.

3. US Department of Health and Human Services. Building successful organizations: workforce planning in HHS. Washington, DC: US Department of Health and Human Services; 1999. Available at: http://www.hhs.gov/ohr/workforce/wfpguide.html. Accessed November 4, 2007.

4. US Census Bureau. US Interim projections by age, sex, race, and Hispanic origin. Washington, DC: US Census Bureau; 2004: Table 1b. Available at: http://www.census.gov/ipc/www/usinterimproj. Accessed October 5, 2007.

5. AHRA *Staff Utilization Survey*. Sudbury, MA: American Healthcare Radiology Administrators; 2006.

6. Evens RG. The impact of new payment systems on the specialty of radiology. *Radiology* 1992;182:613–620.

7. Bhargavan M, Sunshine JH. Workload of radiologists in the United States in 2002–2003 and trends since 1991–1992. *Radiology* 2005;236:920–931.

8. Centers for Medicare and Medicaid Services. Medicare payment systems download. Available at: http://www.cms.hhs.gov/providers/pufdownload/default.asp#rvu. Accessed October 5, 2007.

Bibliography

Aruspex. Operational vs. strategic workforce planning: understanding the difference and when to use each. Available at: http://www.aruspex.com/Operational_Vs_Strategic_WFP.pdf. Accessed February 20, 2008.

McNamara C. Developing your strategic plan. Free Management Library. Available at: http://www.managementhelp.org/fp_progs/sp_mod/str_plan.htm. Accessed February 20, 2008.

Chapter 3

Building Job Descriptions

Gigi Vanacore

> A job description is a document used to provide direction regarding the level of experience,
> educational requirements, and job role expectations for prospective employees applying for
> a specific position. Job descriptions have multiple formats or templates, which can be
> dependent on the organization or its intended purpose. Some of the primary purposes for
> writing a job description are to establish goals for the employee, identify objectives, and provide
> guidelines and direction in a consistent format. A job description also serves as a recruitment
> and performance assessment tool.

Before a new employee can be recruited, selected, or oriented, there must be a guide
to indicate what types of training, skills, and experience are required. A well-defined
job description, created through a process of documentation, job analysis, gathering
detailed information about the job, and aligning responsibilities, is the first step in
a successful recruiting strategy. Much of equal employment opportunity law is inex-
orably bound to the job description as a basic document. Time, money, and effort
spent developing and maintaining job description documents are a good investment. In this chapter, the process of writing a job description is discussed with a
focus on the following:

- Language or terms used
- Job analysis
- Purpose
- Guidelines

Understanding the Language

When preparing to write a job description, it is required to define the actual duties,
job knowledge, skill sets, designated abilities, specific working conditions (including
equipment or systems used), hazards, physical demands, and any other specific
requirements of the job. The first step in developing a job description is an understanding of the language.

A well written job description needs to include separate sections. These sections are
the building blocks for a structured document and will assist in establishing the

general purpose of the document. James R. Lindner, author of the Ohio State University Fact Sheet titled "Writing Job Descriptions for Small Businesses," describes some of the terms used in a job description.[1] Understanding the meaning of the terms used in these sections is important in the developmental stage.

Job Duty

Job duties are work-related functions recognized as specific tasks that, when performed daily, are an integral part of the job. The terms "job duties" and "responsibilities" are interchangeable and, in most documents, divided into primary and secondary responsibilities. It is the main reason why the job exists. Primary duties, sometimes described as the essential duties, can be specific to the job. The body of the document should include 5 to 8 major duties, although if well written it can include as few as 3 major duties. In imaging specific sections or departments such as computed tomography (CT) and ultrasonography, essential duties are classified as the duties or functional skills that are required to operate a scanner or machine. Secondary duties and/or responsibilities are marginal functions of the job. These duties are those identified as performed infrequently and, although important, they are not a fundamental part of the job. These are usually termed as non-essential or marginal duties. Some institutions develop marginal job duties that become part of an organization-specific requirement, such as corporate compliance, injury prevention, privacy, security, and safety training. Attending meetings, participating in quality assurance committees, stocking a room with supplies, or other duties as assigned are included in this category.

Knowledge

Knowledge is information that correlates to the actual duty. In other words, knowledge is a term describing something that the incumbent knows, which, when directly applied to the specific job, demonstrates that the individual knows the subject matter. It simply means that knowledge exemplifies what the applicant needs to know in order to perform the individual job. It is in the knowledge section that the employer should delineate the tasks and talents required to do the job. An example of this in diagnostic imaging would be the requirements on what the applicant must know in order to be hired as a CT technologist. A CT technologist must understand the basic principles of cross-sectional anatomy and must be familiar with the operation of a CT scanner. This section includes information based on what the prospective employee has learned, and it is verifiable through a historical perspective of the incumbent's knowledge/experience.

Skill

A skill is measured through an observable competency. It is the ability for an individual to be able to do something either through natural talents or obtained through education and training. The CT technologist must be able to operate a CT scanner and understand specific procedure protocols. The technologist should recognize and apply imaging parameters and use support equipment such as a power injector, which are required to perform daily duties. The technologist must have a familiarity with cross-sectional anatomy and be familiar with terminology used in correlation with this technology or equipment.

Abilities

This is a focused term related to a particular proficiency proven with a projected outcome. It is results driven. The CT technologist should be able to scan a patient safely and complete the procedure from start to finish. Abilities, measured through general assessments or competencies, serve to evaluate that the technologist can produce a diagnostic and quality scan and prepare it for radiologist interpretation. They must possess the ability to manage the patient through a well documented process, perform safety assessments based on medical history, and select protocols based on the procedure and patient history. The technologist should prepare the scanner, have all supplies at hand, and possess a demonstrated skill and knowledge to complete a study through its entirety.

Specific Requirements

This section includes any additional skills or knowledge identified as essential in order to meet all criteria for the job. These can include credentials, acceptable experience, and level of education, certifications, or licensing. For example, in most states, the general requirement for hiring a CT technologist is certification by the American Registry of Radiology Technologist (ARRT) and/or a state license. Other requirements are an ARRT designated CT certification and the holder of basic cardiac life support or cardiopulmonary resuscitation certificate. When establishing requirements, focus on the minimum skills, education, training, and experience required to perform a job satisfactorily. Do not overstate requirements, as they will limit the applicant pool. Use the term "preferred" rather than "required." In some instances, current employees may be "grandfathered" in the job, and although they may not possess all of the requirements, they are skillful, valuable to the organization, and can still perform the job.

Physical Requirements

The Americans with Disabilities Act (ADA), usually referred to as ADA standards, designates this requirement.[2] The ADA has very specific rules that influence essential duties of a particular job. A job description should include the physical requirements and the work environment and should list any other special requirements in order to comply with the ADA regulations or specifications. If they are not included in the job description, the ADA will not recognize the duties and will interpret this to mean that the incumbent can perform the job in any way they want. All institutions should be familiar with ADA standards and should include them as part of the job description document, as they are the ground rules for labor laws and may serve as the main support source in cases of legal discrimination and prejudice. (These standards are discussed in detail in Chapter 1.)

Job Analysis

Once familiar with the language, the job analysis is the next step in developing and building a job description. During assessment and early stages of the analysis, the author must be knowledgeable about the requirements of the specific job or position under development. There are 3 ways to gather job information: observation, questionnaires, and interviews.[3] Imaging administrators or managers working in conjunction with human resource department staff are the best resources for the initiation and final approval of an analysis. The analysis is obtained by using a type of worksheet/questionnaire template, which will assist in identifying the basic information for the job description, gathering data or information related to the position, and delineating the responsibilities and duties, level of experience, credentials, and other subject matter that must be covered in the job description. The analysis should involve incumbents who perform the duties. It is imperative to engage the staff during a job analysis. Brainstorming will bring a lot of detailed information and will provide specific information from those performing the job. In an imaging setting, the requirements, skill sets, and qualifications that are required to perform specific tasks or job duties are constantly changing based on new technologies, equipment, and medical advancements. Descriptions for each job should be maintained and updated whenever job content, performance requirements, or qualifications change. Because of these factors, it is important that all stakeholders and members of the team be involved in the development process when performing a job analysis. They are the best resources when conducting research during a job analysis.

An analysis should be completed and conducted for each position on a given environment. An environment describes the characteristics or attributes of the job. In an imaging setting, they are departments/areas/modalities such as ultrasonography, CT, magnetic resonance imaging (MRI), interventional imaging, diagnostic imaging, imaging nursing, nuclear medicine, positron emission tomography (PET), breast imaging, scheduling, picture archiving and communications systems (PACS), and other support services. These sections or areas are separate environments, as they each require a different level of experience, expertise, and qualifications. Other settings described as the type of facility, such as a hospital, freestanding center, oncology center, pediatric hospital, emergency care, trauma center, and mobile business, are also relevant to the environment. It is important that every position have its own job description and that it relates to the environment. For example, a CT technologist working in an oncology setting may never see a trauma case. They do not necessarily have to know trauma protocols. However, they must understand lung screening protocols and perform radiation treatment planning or assist during tumor ablation procedures. In this case, the environment will have an impact on the analysis.

Questionnaire

The job analysis should include questions and topics relevant to the position. It is crucial to personalize the questions in order to engage the staff in the process and to evaluate the different levels of performance. The staff will feel that their opinion is important, which enhances performance and cooperation and will provide a sense of ownership. At the same time, the players need to be aware that management and human resource staff will validate the final document and make the final decision of its content due to regulations and to make sure that legal requirements, such as ADA and labor law regulations, are satisfied.[1]

There are several examples available from books and some Internet resources that can assist in creating a job analysis questionnaire. Box 3.1 is a basic sample of a job analysis questionnaire. On his Web site, Ethan Winning has written many articles related to this topic. His article, "The Job Description Questionnaire: Building the Job Description," provides a basic example of a job analysis questionnaire and some useful guidelines that are helpful in demonstrating the format of the worksheet used in the development stages.[4] There are many books written by James E. Neal that relate to this subject. His book, *The #1 Guide to Performance Appraisals: Doing It Right*, covers this topic and provides an excellent job analysis questionnaire example that can be used as a reference as well.[3]

An organization can design the questions depending on the needs or the goals of the institution. To set a casual tone and provide an easy-to-understand document, the questions used in the job analysis can include the use of first, second, or third person pronouns such as you, yours, I, or me.

Job Titles

Another aspect of the job analysis is determination of the title assigned to the position that is to be established. Developing position titles is a challenging task, but many of the regulatory agencies have established titles for technical, support, and

Box 3.1 Basic Sample of a Job Analysis Questionnaire

Name of Institution:

Position:	Department:
Date completed:	Completed by:
Shift:	
New position: _____	Update duties: _____

Job duties:

Essential major duties (critical functions):

1. What are the main duties required to accomplish this job?
2. How often are these duties performed?
3. What specific tasks are required to be done as part of this job?

Marginal or secondary duties (less critical functions):

1. What other duties are not performed frequently but may be completed as part of this job?
2. List any behavioral competencies or other duties that may help to achieve this job.

Job knowledge (specific responsibilities):

1. What type of knowledge is needed to perform this job?
2. Does this job require decision making?
3. What is the level of supervision required for this job? How many people are supervised?
4. Does this job require any equipment operation or specific tasks that require direction and guidance?

Job skills:

1. Does this job require specialized training?
2. Does the job require computer skills, any special software, and/or hardware?
3. Does the job require any specific knowledge of technology or terminology?

Job abilities:

1. What does the employee need to know to perform the job?
2. Are there any competencies that would be required to be met?
3. Can the tasks be evaluated through competencies or specific proficiency measurements?

Job requirements:

1. What level of experience is required for this job?
2. Are there any credentials, certifications, or licensing requirements required to perform this job? Preferred versus required?
3. Does this job require completion of a specific field of study?
4. Are there any minimum requirements for this position?

Physical requirements (working conditions):

1. What physical demands are essential to perform this job?
2. Are there any reasonable accommodations that can be made to enable a person with disabilities to perform these tasks?

3. What physical exertion is required to do the job (eg, lifting, pulling, pushing, or bending)?
4. What is the limit of physical exertion? List the percentage of time spent sitting, standing, and walking.
5. Are there any environmental conditions in the work area (eg, exposure to radiation, magnetic fields, patient contact, cold or dark environment)?
6. List any specific requirements regarding vision, hearing, manual dexterity, handling objects, speaking clearly.

Comments to support any additional requirements:

Indicate any contacts that this position may be required to communicate or deal directly with:

Internal: Coworkers, peers, subordinates, department heads, visitors, patients and their family members, faculty, physicians.
External: Customers, state agencies, professional organizations, community physicians, vendors, technical schools, students.

Give an example of an employee with comparable functions, if applicable.

Job analysis reviewed by (should be a supervisor or manager)

Name: Date:

Signature:

I certify that the statements included in this document represent, to the best of my knowledge, an accurate description of the duties for this position.

Second review: Optional

Name: Date:

Signature

Approved:

Name   Date:

Signature:

Submitted: Date:

nursing positions that exist in diagnostic imaging. Some professional organizations, like the ones listed below, can also be of assistance when researching position titles in an imaging environment.

- American Registry for Radiologic Technologists (ARRT)
- American Registry for Diagnostic Medical Sonography (ARDMS)
- American Healthcare Radiology Administrators (AHRA)
- American College of Radiology Imaging Network (ACRIN)
- Nuclear Medicine Technology Certification Board (NMTCB)
- American Radiological Nurses Association (ARNA)
- Cardiovascular Credentialing International (CCI)

The Dictionary of Occupational Titles (DOT) is another excellent resource for position titles. The DOT Web site includes occupational titles that refer to the term "occupation" as "a collective description of individual jobs performed with minor variations in many establishments."[5] According to DOT, there are 7 parts to an occupational definition. Listed in order, they are the occupational code number, occupational title, industry designation, alternate titles, body of the definition, undefined related titles, and definition trailer. In the body of the definition, there are 3 parts: the lead statement, task elements statement, and the "may" items (which relate to duties that may be required of workers in a particular position and may be adopted by one organization but not others). Complete details on the 7 parts to an occupational definition are found on the Web site and are a great starting and resource point. The code 32919 lists the "radiologic technologist" job description and related duties.[5]

Salary Grades

Salary grades are often associated with job descriptions. They are structured pay plans that include salaries in a given pay range. They correspond with position titles and designate a minimum and maximum pay scale that is based on credentials, experience, and/or expertise. They are highly dependent on geographical regions and locations, as well as the market demand for the position. Market reports and job grades or classifications are to be supported by using legitimate survey resources such as the Watson Wyatt survey, Radford survey, Virginia nurses survey, or the Mercer information technology survey. Public access information can be easily accessed through Internet surveys from such sources as AHRA, AuntMinnie.com, and Salary.com. Local or national job postings are also a great resource of information. A salary grade is often listed with an assigned numerical symbol in the human resource department and many public postings do not disclose the actual true quantitative value of the salary. For example, the salary grade assigned a level 6 is given a minimum, midpoint, and maximum salary amount. Most institutions will display salary grades but will keep actual salary ranges or amounts confidential, as they provide the employer with a marketing tool and a competitive advantage. For more on this topic, see Chapter 7.

Purpose of the Job Description

Once a job analysis has been completed, the next step is to identify the purpose for the job description. The human resource department in conjunction with management staff has the authority to determine the purpose of the job descriptions. In his book, *The #1 Guide to Performance Appraisals: Doing It Right,* James E. Neal mentions that a job description provides an organization with structure and makes effective use of resources and promotes collaboration.[3] He also states that it provides an organization with structure for achieving productivity and makes effective use of resources.[3] Primarily, there are two important goals that the job description supports: to provide guidance and clear expectations for employees and to be used to recruit the right candidate for the job.

During the recruitment process, the job description will function as a tool to delineate the expectations of the job. It will also serve as a document to keep the recruitment focused on the level of responsibility required for the job; it can set clear expectations and establish supervision criteria, expected training, and required qualifications. It will identify the experience and knowledge requirements for the job and serve to describe critical/essential duties. The job description can also help formalize the interview process as it can serve as a guide. To current employees, it functions as a reference tool; they know what their job is, and there are no assumptions made. It delineates levels of responsibility, assists in setting job expectations, and indicates the level of experience and qualifications to support the continuation of the job.

Performance Appraisal/Evaluation Tool
When a job description is used as a performance evaluation tool, the job description must include clear duty and skill requirements, professional requirements, and a basic list of required competencies. James E. Neal refers to this topic as "standards of performance." He states that each section of the job description, if used to rate employees, must be given a "quantitative measurement." The tool may include a combination of percentile, textual, numerical, objective based, and/or behavioral rating systems.[3] A percentage rating assigned to each duty may delineate the value of each duty to be performed or it can weigh the difficulty or importance of the duty or even the expected time to be spent performing an individual task. Specific terms

found in these descriptions include words such as average, below average, satisfactory, unsatisfactory, meets standards, does not meet standards, and below standards. Some institutions also use job descriptions for peer and employee self-evaluations. Performance must be measurable, clearly defined, observable, consistent, and based on the job.

Merit Reviews

Interchangeably merged with the performance appraisal tool, many job descriptions are combined to serve together as a merit review. The tool should include sections classified by a point or percentage rating system. In this case, the job description sections are assigned a particular point or rating measurement used to evaluate the employee on a yearly basis. Merit reviews serve to provide feedback and assessment using the same format as the performance evaluation tool, which can include specific behavioral objectives. Behavioral objectives are based on observable behavior such as being a team player, service oriented and customer focused, responsible, positive, professional, adaptable, and committed to excellence. The combination of performance evaluation and merit rating is the most common use of the job description in healthcare settings and many large organizations.

Compensation

The job description should include the level of experience or education requirements of the job. Compensation can be set based on the credentials, years of experience in a specialty, and/or professional category of the prospective employee. Positions can also be established and paid at a higher rate or grade than others based on local or nationally driven market surveys, salary surveys, and other resources. The human resource department has the responsibility in organizations to assist in developing and researching appropriate compensation plans. A well-written job description is one of the best compensation support tools and resources for an organization.

Training

Although not used often in the imaging environment, job descriptions are a resource to train new employees. This type of job description requires a lot of detail, and its general purpose is to provide very specific guidelines and detailed descriptions of all duties.

General Guidelines

Once the purpose(s) of the job description has been established and the job analysis completed, the components of the job description can be developed. To build the components and language of the job description, it is imperative that all feedback received during the job analysis is evaluated for accuracy. Managers, administrators, and the human resource department have the responsibility to spend time reviewing the content and adding any additional comments or supporting details.

The content of the job description is very important. The terminology and written statements play a role in the logic and translation of the content by employees. The job description should include action verbs and wording that is not too specific or vague.[1] Many resources are available that provide examples of statements used in job descriptions; these can be found on the Internet, with the Department of Labor, the DOT, books, and other resources. The University of California at Santa Barbara has a link on their Web site that provides a glossary of terms and is very useful when selecting words to use when describing duties and responsibilities.[6] The DOT provides hundreds of job titles and job descriptions, including those used in imaging environments, nursing, and other support services.

There are several components that are commonly included as part of the job description document. Although different formats of the document may be designed or used, these components provide general guidelines regardless of what institution or environment they are to be used for. All job descriptions should include the following:

- Name of the organization
- Position title/salary grade
- Description of the job/job summary
- Reporting structure
- Basic list of external and internal contacts
- Job knowledge and responsibilities
    - Essential duties
    - Marginal duties
- Organization specific responsibilities
- Qualifications, education, and/or skill set (list whether required or preferred)
- Physical requirements
- Working conditions (including equipment and systems used) and hazards

See Box 3.2 for a sample job description.

Box 3.2 Sample Job Description

The Imaging Hospital

Position title: Ultrasound technologist

Description of the job: Performs specialized technical duties that require the ability to obtain 2 dimensional ultrasound recordings of internal organs for the detection, diagnosis, and evaluation of disease using ultrasound equipment.

Reports to: Ultrasound Supervisor
Imaging Manager
Imaging Chief of Service

Contacts: Hospital staff, vendors, service personnel, patients, visitors, internal and external physicians, research staff, students, and other affiliates.

Essential duties and responsibilities:

- Selects the appropriate equipment and is aware of the set up based on procedure protocol, specifications, and standards.
- Selects, prepares, and sets up ultrasound equipment and supplies including transducers.
- Capable of selecting and adjusting equipment and controls based on the anatomy in question to be scanned, field of depth, patient evaluation, and other specifications.
- Moves transducer by hand over the specified anatomy, observes sound wave displays to provide a written assessment, and discusses findings with the attending radiologist or resident.
- Evaluates the technical quality of images and is able to record, archive, retrieve, compile, and calculate data.
- Independently capable of assisting the radiologist during invasive procedures such as biopsies and abscess drainages.
- Can independently perform all ultrasound-related studies as well as Doppler studies, deep abdominal scanning, and vascular examinations.
- Positions the patient based on anatomy in question and provides accurate measurements, educates and can clearly explain procedures before scanning, and follows age-specific guidelines.
- Cleans and sterilizes transducers and supplies.
- Practices positive patient identification.

Marginal duties:

- Stocks and replenishes supplies as needed.
- Calibrates and performs equipment maintenance.
- Participates in continuous quality improvement activities or committees.
- Attends staff meetings as required and reads staff meeting minutes.
- Serves as a preceptor to students if required.

Organization-specific responsibilities:

- Adheres to dress code requirements and standards.
- Completes annual competencies and educational requirements.

- Maintains patient confidentiality in compliance with the Health Insurance Portability and Accountability Act (HIPAA)
- Wears identification badge while on duty.
- Adheres to the organization mission, policies, ethics, cultural diversity, patient safety, and other related goals.
- Promotes a culture of safety, quality services, and customer satisfaction.
- Exhibits a positive image and professional conduct and is willing to adapt to changes in the institutional roles and needs.
- Performs and/or accepts other duties as assigned.

Qualifications/skill set:

- Two year allied health degree with 1 year successful completion of an approved ultra-sound program.
- Eligibility or ARDMS registered is preferred.
- Current Basic Cardiac Life Support (BCLS) certification.
- Experience with basic personal computer or Windows operating system.
- Knowledge of general anatomy, physiology, and medical terminology.

Physical requirements or work conditions:

- This position has specific ADA standards that include vision, hearing, repetitive motion, manual dexterity, and lifting and pulling of objects.
- Ability to communicate and read in English.
- This position requires working in an environment that can pose a potential risk to exposure to infectious diseases and agents.

Approved by:

Issued:

Revised:

Conclusion

A well constructed job description should be a realistic representation of the job. (See Sidebar 3.1 for tips to remember when writing job descriptions.) There are several steps in developing a job description. It is not an easy process and writing them can be time consuming, but it is well worth the effort. For the employee, it provides structure, direction, and consistent goals to achieve; delineates duties; promotes solidarity; and sets responsibilities. For the employer, it provides tools for measuring performance to enhance productivity, human resource planning, selection, training and development, and employee compensation, and gives consistent direction and delineates regulatory requirements. Managers should conduct a job analysis whenever a job changes. It is common practice that once a job description is developed, it is ideal to update it frequently (at least once per year). The job

SIDEBAR 3.1: Tips to Remember

Below are tips that may prove useful when writing job descriptions:

- Focus on the facts, be concise and clear
- Decide on the format
- Summarize responsibilities
- Identify level of responsibility
- Indicate and include all duties related to the job
- Use the job description to provide direction
- Provide consistent guidelines
- Involve employees in the development and updating of job descriptions
- Update and revise the job description often and at a minimum of once per year
- Do not write a job description that is too specific or with high expectations
- Job descriptions provide control and direction to the employees
- Make sure that the duties and information apply directly to the job
- Set clear education requirements
- Include all of the basic components of the job description
- Use appropriate action verbs such as scans, performs, exhibits, documents, organizes, reports, assigns, executes, reviews, records, handles, and demonstrates
- Be brief and clear, do not overstate any requirements or duties
- Include any other special requirements such as critical thinking, supervision, training, or language skills
- Always include primary and secondary responsibilities

description should be accurate and reflect changes in the job market. In recent years, the job market and technological changes in imaging have exploded. Technologies such as PET, 64-slice CT, 3-T magnetic resonance digital imaging, digital mammography, and PACS have been introduced. Many institutions have eliminated the need for processors because of the digital imaging revolution. There have also been new drug discoveries to be aware of, new management techniques to be analyzed, and the advent of virtual and molecular imaging to be explored. As new equipment and new technologies are developed, job duties and expectations change. New rules such as those delineated by HIPAA, which drive how patient information, computer health information, and electronic patient medical records are managed, also play a role in how duties are performed. The Joint Commission's national standards of performance has also changed the role of staff within an imaging environment.

There are many books and Web sites available as resources. According to an excerpt from the *Job Description Handbook* written by Margie Mader-Clark, "a well-thought-out job description provides you and the employees who report to you with a blueprint for success."[7] The job description is a tool that enhances performance and productivity, delineates authority, sets expectations, and promotes success within an organization.

References

1. Lindner JR. *Writing Job Descriptions for Small Businesses*. Ohio State University Fact Sheet. Columbus, OH: Ohio State University, 2005.

2. ADA home page. Americans with Disabilities Act. Available at: http://www.ada.gov. Accessed January 8, 2008.

3. Neal JE Jr. *The #1 Guide to Performance Appraisals: Doing It Right*. 5th print. Perrysburg, OH: Neal Publications, Inc., 2004.

4. Winning EA. The job description questionnaire: building the job description, 1998–2006. Availabe at: http://www.ewin.com. Accessed January 8, 2008.

5. Dictionary of Occupational Titles. Available at: http://www.occupationalinfo.org/onet/32919.html. Accessed January 8, 2008.

6. University of California Santa Barbara, Human Resources Department. Glossary of terms. Available at: http://hr.ucsb.edu/comp/glossary.php. Accessed January 8, 2008.

7. Mader-Clark M. *Job Description Handbook*. Chapter 1. Berkeley, CA: NOLO Publishing, 2006.

Bibliography

American Registry for Diagnostic Medical Sonography. Available at: http://www.ardms.org.

American Registry of Radiology Technologists. Available at: http://www.arrt.org.

Department of Labor, Bureau of Labor Statistic. Available at: http://www.bls.gov.

Equal Employment Opportunity Commission. Available at: http://www.eeoc.gov/policy/ada.html.

Health Insurance Portability and Accountability Act (HIPAA). Available at: http://www.hipaa.org.

H. Lee Moffitt Cancer Center & Research Institute. *Radiology Policies and Procedure Manual*. Tampa, FL: University of South Florida, 2006.

The Joint Commission. Available at: http://www.jointcommission.org.

2 Human Resource Recruitment

In this section:

Chapter 4

Find the Talent

Peter C. McCormack

Recruitment of qualified personnel and the ultimate goal of retention is the common thread that binds every imaging facility to their respective human resource department. This relationship, built on open communication and a keen understanding of the current labor market, will enable imaging facilities to adequately and, most importantly, accurately staff for immediate and long range needs.

Although technologist recruitment has been with the imaging industry since its inception, it has become a paramount issue in recent years. The phenomenal expansion in imaging studies, fueled by an increasingly growing and aging population, has created numerous unfilled vacancies. As with other industries, the recruitment cycle in imaging experiences peaks and valleys. Since the beginning of the millennium, a decline in the number of high school graduates coupled with a wealth of career alternatives (eg, computer industry, electronics) has contributed to a dwindling pool of potential technologists. This shortfall of potential healthcare employees has created a crisis, in some areas, and shows few signs of abating. Penny M. Olivi predicted in a 2004 *Radiology Management* article that the "worst staffing crisis ever experienced in radiologic technology will take place in the next 4 or more years."[1] Many factors contribute to the ongoing recruitment dilemma:

- Decline in imaging technology programs, both at the community college level and, most acutely, hospital based certification courses, mainly due to the lack of qualified instructors as the Joint Review Committee on Education in Radiologic Technology has mandated that program directors must have, as a minimum, a master's degree effective January 1, 2002 (Standard 6.1 Human Resources—Standards for an Accredited Educational Program in Radiologic Sciences). This directive has had a substantial impact on imaging technology programs throughout the country, especially the smaller ones, as most instructors either have an associate's or a bachelor's degree. Some instructors have chosen to return to the field, retire, or select an alternative occupation as the cost and time necessary to complete a master's program proved daunting.
- Reluctance on the part of seasoned technologists to accept management positions, a direct result of the lack of a defined career ladder in most departments.

- Trepidation concerning salary—an unwillingness to accept a salaried position, especially if their current hourly income plus overtime exceeds that of a management position.
- Unwillingness of senior leadership to mentor potential supervisors.
- Expanding roles of an imaging assistant/extender allows for an avenue of advancement and career satisfaction that would appeal to the experienced technologist.
- Appeal of flexibility and increased salary by hiring on as a locum tenens (commonly referred to as a "traveler").
- At this point in history, there are 4 very distinct generations in the workplace: The Depression Generation (born 1909–1945), Baby Boomers (born 1946–1964), Generation X (born 1965–1979), and the Millennials (born 1980–2000). Each group presents different challenges with regard to intrinsic core values, leadership needs, and definition of success.

The *New York Times* reported that healthcare is the "single strongest sector in the United States economy today."[2] For those workers in high demand, the current economic climate is great news; for employers desperate to fill positions with qualified personnel, the news is greeted with less enthusiasm. More than 250,000 diagnostic imaging technologists, nuclear medicine technologists, sonographers, and radiation therapists are currently employed in the United States, but thousands more will be needed to keep up with the growing demand for their services. The US Bureau of Labor Statistics estimates that there will be 75,000 more technologists needed in 2010 than in 2000 due to the number of positions and decreases in the existing pool.[3]

It is important to understand the costs correlated with terminating and replacing talented technologists. Direct department costs include[4]:

- Advertising for the new position
- Reviewing resumes
- Interviewing and testing candidates
- Conducting orientation for and training of new hires

If an imaging administrator makes a mistake in hiring (usually realized within the first 6 months of hire), the cost of replacing that technologist can be as high as 2.5 times the individual's annual salary, especially if a locum tenens is needed. In addition to an inflated hourly rate, the manager may need to factor in travel expenses, housing, and/or a per diem. A technologist earning $40,000 has the potential of costing the department $100,000 (Table 4.1).

Table 4.1 Cost of Terminating and Replacing a Technologist

Technologist Position	Average Annual Salary (approximate)*	Estimated Locum Tenens Expenses (2.5 × standard annual salary)	Annual Difference
Diagnostic imaging	$52,000	$130,000	$78,000
Mammography	$57,000	$142,500	$85,500
Magnetic resonance imaging	$62,000	$155,000	$93,000

*Source: American Society of Radiologic Technologists Wage and Salary Survey, June 2007.

For a director of a 500 bed academic research hospital, a 35 bed rural community hospital, or a freestanding MRI center, the continued success of the organization is directly related to the people hired. It has been said many times and in a multitude of ways, people are the most important asset.

Recruitment Methods

Direct Mail

A traditional method of recruitment with varying degrees of effectiveness is direct mail. Relatively inexpensive to produce and easy to edit, this is a mainstay of many organizations. Desktop publishing software allows organizations to print professional grade correspondence that has brand recognition. Direct mail lists of technologists and students can be obtained from state and regional societies and imaging technology programs. Direct mail may be tailored for the department's various specialties, and those technologists that have specific qualifications and are certified in their respective discipline (eg, ultrasound, mammography, and interventional services) can be targeted. Depending on the local job market, success may be somewhat limited depending on the number of hospitals, clinics, and independent imaging facilities in the catchment area as they are often competing for the same population of technologists. Another factor that may influence a recruitment campaign is location; in general, rural areas have experienced more difficulty in attracting technologists compared with more urban locales.

Guidelines for direct mail:

- Learn from advertisers. Study marketing concepts and utilize successful methods to reach the desired audience.
- Go "first class." First class mail that is undeliverable is returned to sender. There may be significant savings by obtaining a discount from the mailing list broker if that route is taken.

- Hand address or directly print on the envelope to avoid mailing labels that look impersonal.
- Use envelopes to enclose the direct mail piece as this not only will protect the literature, but will also increase the chance it will be opened and read. Avoid correspondence that is folded (a self mailer) as it will look too commercial and runs the risk of being discarded by the candidate.
- Personalize! Include the name and proper credentials in the copy.
- Make it easy for the candidate to respond. Prominently highlight a toll free number or employment hotline, or include a postage paid reply card.

When evaluated against other recruitment methods, direct mail in the current labor environment has proven to be a "double edged sword," as it can be a cost effective adjunct to recruitment or a complete bust. Empirical statistics reveal a response rate of 0% to 8%.[5] If there is no response using other methods of recruitment, 1% to 8% may in some circumstances be considered a success.

Costs are variable when using direct mail (Table 4.2).

Newspapers

Contrary to what people may hear or see on television or the Internet, printed media will not disappear. Many newspapers and community bulletins throughout

Table 4.2 Direct Mail Costs

Direct Mail	Expenses (1000/2500 candidates)
Professional society mailing list	$3000/$3000
First class mail (at $0.373, discounted) + annual mailing fee	$373/$933 $175/$175
Design work (may be eliminated if using desktop publishing software)	$1500/$1500
Printing expense at $1.10 per piece (literature printed professionally; if done in house, add cost of paper and ink)	$1100/$2750
Envelopes at $25 per box of 500	$50/$125
Labor (addressing and stuffing envelopes by clerical staff; $12 × 8 hrs/$12 × 20 hrs)	$96/$240
Total Costs	
Professional	**$6294/$8723**
In house (approximate)	**$3694/$4473**

First Class mail rates per United States Postal Service current as of September 2007. Additional costs per Scott & White Marketing Department, July 2007.

the nation have not only survived the technology revolution, but have managed to prosper by maintaining and, in some markets, expanding readership by providing timely information in an appealing consumer format.

Guidelines for newspaper advertising:

- The help wanted section of the paper has limited candidate appeal; people who read this section are either unemployed, unhappy, or both. Hiring managers want to appeal to the person who is gainfully employed and relatively happy. Therefore, advertise in other sections where people are browsing. These ads stand out and attract more attention than the small ads found in the "help wanted" section.
- There are numerous carriers other than the local daily paper. Check out the *CareerMart*, found in the *PennySaver*. College and vocational newspapers are an option, as are professional organization papers.
- Think graphics. Use color and white space effectively.
- Use powerful advertising copy.

Images may capture briefly, but it is the printed word that will generate a response. Successful ads incorporate the following into their copy:

- Word-of-mouth advertising into testimonials
- The phrase "you will" rather than the ambiguous "you should" or "you will be expected to"
- Present tense
- Highlighted attention words: *"new equipment"* and *"increased shift differential"*
- Personalized style, writing from a "you" point of view

Most of the nation's newspapers have established Web sites that also include an extensive advertising supplement of which a "help wanted" section is often a prominent feature. Also, there are a number of national media companies that have a presence in many cities and own many newspapers. Help wanted ads placed in one newspaper in one city may be electronically accessed via the Internet throughout the country. A typical ad package is outlined in Table 4.3.

Online

The imaging industry has embraced the Internet since its infancy and nearly all organizations associated with the field are represented online. Of interest to the employer and the potential employee are significant Internet stalwarts of the industry: AuntMinnie, UltrasoundJobs, RTJobs, MedHunters, and numerous others that post positions on a contractual basis (weekly, monthly). Professional organizations, including the American Society of Radiologic Technologists (ASRT),

Table 4.3 Typical Employment Ad Packages

Print and Online Premium	Online Only	Print and Online
30 day enhanced listing online (Careerbuilder)	30 day enhanced listing online (Careerbuilder)	—
Newspaper online 30 days	Newspaper online 30 days	Newspaper online 7 days
Classified 2 days (Sun/Wed)	—	Classified 2 days (Sun/Wed)
Starting at $444 for 3 lines, each additional line $48	Starting at $419 for online only	Starting at $339 for 3 lines, each additional line $48

Careerbuilder is owned by Tribune Company, McClatchy, Gannett, and Mircosoft. Rates current as of September 2007.

American Institute of Ultrasound in Medicine, and AHRA should not be discounted. These Web sites are accessed daily by thousands of people and enjoy the distinction of being able to reach a far flung readership almost instantaneously. The Internet is a recruiter's dream; no other medium has the ability to quickly reach a targeted audience.

Guidelines for online advertising:

- What is the size and scope of the Web site? Does it have an extremely large readership or is it a smaller subset of the profession?
- Is the site user friendly? Easy to navigate? Can a user get to the ad quickly? Is there a lot of scrolling through banner advertisements? Select a site that allows for ease of navigation.
- Is the ad cost effective? Determine the target readership, review the advertising budget, and arrive at a decision prudently.
- Predetermine the method of contact with the candidate (ad box, blind, or direct). Select a method that will not discourage the candidate from applying and, at the same time, protects the interests of the organization.

In the advertising copy, whether print or electronic, tout the facility's awards and achievements (eg, *U.S. News & World Report* Top 100 Hospitals, Solucient Top 15 Teaching Hospital, etc). If applicable, mention research conducted and a list of journals published.

If the facility is in a position to boast about its technology, do so. Make mention of the newly installed 3T magnet or the high definition CT scanner. Highlight the city's or area's attributes, for example: urban versus rural, convenient access to recreational, sports, and cultural activities. Include cost-of-living information or local school ratings to make the area attractive to qualified out-of-town applicants. In addition, provide as much information as possible on financial incentives and benefits. Many facilities are reluctant to state salary ranges as it is proprietary, but it may be prudent to let the candidate know where the salaries at a facility rank in comparison to other institutions similar in size and scope.

Advertising online can be extremely advantageous to the organization that needs to publish an opening quickly. The process of placing an ad is easy. After logging on to the desired Web site, all are menu driven and provide the instructions for registration, placement, and payment of the ad. When considering online advertising, select the one that meets the organization's needs. If advertising for a sonographer, UltrasoundJobs would be a logical choice as the site is specific to the discipline. The search for a registered technologist may encompass placing an ad with AuntMinnie or RTJobs (or both).

The generic employment search engines (Monster, Careerbuilder, YahooJobs) are also available. These sites host thousands of employment ads and are well known to the general public. Although, these sites are generally the venue for broad scope positions. If the need is for a special skill set, the manager may be best served by using the Web sites associated with the professional societies for the specific discipline.

Online advertising costs are outlined in Table 4.4, and see Sidebar 4.1 for use of blind ads.

Job Fairs

The primary purpose of a job fair is to obtain as many applications from interested and qualified candidates as possible and to introduce the facility as an employer of choice. Job fairs are location flexible; they can be utilized locally, regionally, and nationally.

Table 4.4 Online Advertising Costs

Web Site	Cost	Timeline
AuntMinnie	$225	1 month, 1 job posting
RTJobs	$250	60 days, 1 job posting
UltrasoundJobs	$400	60 days, 1 job posting
ASRT	$195	30 days, 1 job posting
Monster	$950	2 week 100 mile resume search, 1 job posting
	$1225	2 week national resume search, 1 job posting

All Web site rates current as of September 2007.

SIDEBAR 4.1: Blind Ads

If an organization is nationally recognized as an "employer of choice," it can be assured that its reputation is a definite plus in attracting top candidates. However, if the organization does not enjoy that image, the blind ad (either in the newspaper or online) may be considered. A blind ad is an advertisement that does not identify the institution and requests that candidates send their resume to a post office box. Well known facilities will sometimes use a blind ad for the opposite reason; they do not want to be inundated with responses, and it allows them to be more selective. The historic response to blind ads is limited, mainly because the candidates fear that the organization to which they are applying may be their own.

Appropriate criteria for blind ads:

- Security maintenance. When an employee is being terminated and a search is initiated for a replacement.
- When a facility needs to add to its pool of potential workers.
- Adding specific positions or replacing employees during an organizational layoff.

Be cognizant that blind ads tend to diminish response rates among candidates who are currently satisfied with their current employment, and the potentially stellar applicants being sought may not apply because of the concern of contacting their present employer. Use blind ads judiciously.

Generally in radiology, job fairs are held at educational institutions, state and national society meetings, or in conjunction with a facility's human resource department in various venues such as a local or regional chamber of commerce sponsored event.

To achieve success using a job fair as a recruitment strategy, it is important to have a clear understanding of the target audience and the positions the organization is attempting to fill. Attendance at a job fair does not necessarily produce a good return on investment if the strategy is to collect a large number of applications without a defined plan. In the hospital industry, job fairs are best utilized when there is a specific position to fill and managers can capitalize on the opportunity to meet with those interested individuals that possess the skill set needed to close the vacancy.

Job fairs require cooperation between the imaging manager and department and professional human resource representatives. Participating in job fairs has its challenges—long hours, the feeling of being "on stage," time away from the department—but if conducted with proper planning, they can be extremely rewarding. Job fairs have proven to be an effective recruitment tool—thorough planning, delivery of the message, and timely follow up are key ingredients to the success of this endeavor.

Guidelines for job fairs:

- Attend the right job fair. The chances of success will be quite limited if a booth is set up at a respiratory therapist convention. Job fairs can be an expensive outing when travel expenses and personnel time are factored in.
- Managers will be kicking themselves in the "booth" if they are setting up with a table-cloth, a solitary display poster, and a small stack of handouts while their competitors are wowing potential candidates with state-of-the-art multimedia displays, color handouts, and giveaways. Do the homework; find out what is needed to be competitive. There are several companies that specialize in these products and the costs ($2000 to $5000 price range) can be spread among other departments within the organization as they are designed for multiple recruitment purposes. Whatever type of booth is decided on, consider the ease of setup, storage, and shipping.
- Talk the talk. Staff the booth with individuals (qualified human resource representatives or technologists) who can sell the candidate on employment opportunities with the department. Listless, apathetic people manning the booth can destroy efforts. Use high energy representatives, create a buzz.
- Encourage attendees to stop by the booth. Do not neglect giveaways: prizes, small gifts, or a prize drawing. Check with the corporate compliance officer before the job fair to avoid violating any state or federal regulations concerning this type of recruitment (generally a defined monetary value cannot be exceeded). If sanctioned, a prize drawing can be an effective tool. It not only generates traffic, but can also offer an opportunity to catalogue the participant's demographics. This information can be used to send out letters thanking them for taking the time to visit and, if necessary, supply them with additional information about employment opportunities with the organization.
- Provide an alternative. The aftermath of Hurricane Katrina left many hospitals and clinics severely damaged and in some cases completely destroyed. The impact on healthcare workers cannot be understated; many either lost their jobs or through necessity were forced to work reduced hours and faced an uncertain employment future. Some hospitals in surrounding states, confronted with a shortage of qualified technologists, traveled to these stricken areas to recruit displaced workers. Provided with generous relocation and assistance packages, many workers made the decision to move, which ultimately benefited both parties.

See Sidebar 4.2 for using local schools as job fairs.

Staffing Services

There are occasions when it is exceedingly difficult to fill an employment position with a qualified technologist. In no other industry is there an overwhelming need for this type of expediency as healthcare, the collective mission of providing patient care demands no less.

Hiring managers face a quandary: conduct an all out advertising blitz when the clock is against them or utilize the services of a staffing agency. Although this method of recruitment will have the potential to negatively impact the staffing budget, at times there is no other choice. Fortunately, there are numerous staffing agencies available that specialize in placing imaging specific workers. This is another example of the usefulness of the Internet, although an organization's human resource department may already have an established business relationship with an agency.

The staffing agency will need position details: the ceiling rate the organization is willing to pay (including shift differential and on-call pay), start date, the number of weeks needed, equipment used, and other job oriented information. An important caveat to remember is the staffing agency is accountable for the employees they recommend. For a manager to make an informed decision, the staffing firm will need to provide, in addition to references, past performance evaluations. Do advance research; make sure to pay only for those services needed and play hardball if they are providing services not wanted or needed. The staffing world is extremely competitive and many agencies will reduce their rates for the following reasons:

- The manager agrees to offer the staffing service an exclusive (work only with them).
- There are multiple positions to fill.
- Management declares up front that they agree to pay a certain rate and adhere to it.

The onus is on the staffing agency to provide the organization with a suitable candidate as they operate within a very competitive market. Their continued existence is dependent on placing the right person. It is incumbent on the manager to properly interview the prospective candidate to determine if there is a good fit. Qualifications alone do not spell success; there is the all important matter of personal chemistry and the ability to adapt to the institutional culture. Also, be aware of the subject of salary rearing its ugly head if the permanent staff discovers what a locum tenens is being paid. There is no department immune from this discussion. This discourse will no doubt give the manager an opportunity to display professional human relations acumen. Be prepared and attempt to deflect this temporary hiring situation from polarizing staff by reminding them of the positive aspects of their employment (stability, wider range of benefits, and a sense of "home").

Open House

An open house can be held in a department, staffed by volunteer employees and human resource personnel. This event provides an opportunity for interested employees to check the operation out in an informal, hassle free manner. This has particular appeal to candidates who do not want to engage in a formal job interview or those who are happy in their present position, but are curious to see what is available.

Open houses can make excellent business sense if there are multiple positions to fill, as cost-per-hire reductions can be made as expenses associated with job fairs and outside advertising are mitigated. Actual costs are minor, perhaps 2 to 3 hours overtime (ask for volunteers first) for the staff, refreshments, giveaways, and literature. Another plus is the savings realized by not having transportation and shipping expenses.

Guidelines for an open house:

■ Advertise in the local and regional newspapers. Contact the local imaging technology program. Provide a direct call-in number to schedule an appointment; this allows questions candidates may have about the job and the organization to be answered. Since many technologists network and may be concerned about being seen by a colleague or an acquaintance of their current employer, have the direct call-in number answered by the department manager or a qualified team member to schedule a time that assures the candidate's privacy is safeguarded.
■ Hosting the event at the organization, rather than a hotel, is a good choice, especially if the facility is equipped with the latest state-of-the-art equipment. The candidates are not going to leave with a favorable impression if held outside of the organization—they are there to kick the tires.

- Enough people should be on hand to provide an individual escort for a tour. Conduct a dry run, determine the time needed to give a tour, and answer questions.
- Involve technologists in addition to supervisory staff. They are often the best ambassadors. Be sure to educate them on selling points so they are comfortable speaking to the candidates.
- Offer refreshments, prizes, and literature. Make guests feel welcome, give away inexpensive prizes, and make department-specific and organizational literature readily available.
- Consider the flow. Determine how each candidate will be greeted. Plan the tour route and how the event should be wrapped up.

Give candidates the opportunity to complete an application form before leaving. Think about the goals of the open house, the impression to get across, and plan accordingly.

Campus Recruitment

It is with certainty that recruiting efforts will concentrate on community colleges and vocational programs offering a curriculum culminating in either an associate in science (AS degree in imaging technology, ultrasound, nuclear medicine) or a certification program (both eligible to take the American Registry of Radiologic Technologists exam) or other disciplines such as Registered Diagnostic Medical Sonographer or Certified Nuclear Medicine Technologist.

Guidelines for campus recruitment:

- Does the curriculum match the skill set needed by the department?
- What is the student demographic? The last 2 decades have seen an increase in the number of displaced older workers returning to school. There is an excellent probability that the organization will not be recruiting students 2 years removed from high school.
- What is the typical size of the graduating class? Are there enough students available to join the staff?
- Where is the school located? Is it in a transient region where students have to move after graduation or do they tend to remain in the area? This may work to an advantage in either scenario.
- Is there a successful history of recruitment with the school? If it is a new relationship, is it worth the time and resources? This may provide an opportunity for both parties to establish a mutually beneficial relationship, capitalizing on the good will that is present when beginning a new venture.

- Are there competing organizations? If the school has a long term relationship with another hospital, it may not be worth the effort.
- Grow your own. Negotiate and insert a clause into any agreement that allows for local students with the required academic requirements satisfied to be placed in the program. Local students are more likely to remain in the area where they have family.

The most important ingredients for campus recruitment success are to become actively involved in developing relationships with the school's professional staff. The organization can become involved by:

- Contributing money, equipment, and time
- Volunteering to sit on the advisory board
- Jointly sponsoring open houses, job and career fairs
- Teaching a class or giving periodic presentations
- Sponsoring a scholarship
- Jointly developing a clinical internship program for the students
- Offering a clinical fellowship for each modality

The object of fostering a relationship with a school is to develop a pipeline for the employment of their graduates. Start early; do not concentrate efforts on those students who are near graduation. By building a relationship before students start the program, and staying involved for the entire 2 years, an organization will ultimately benefit by creating an environment where the newly minted technologists will want to work for the organization.

Expenses associated with campus recruitment can vary due to the degree of personal or professional involvement:

- Donation of equipment may be advantageous if eligible for tax write-off
- Scholarship funding
- Time spent away from the department (advisory or teaching capacity)
- Joint venture career and job fairs

Employee Referral
One of the most effective ways to attract qualified technologists is employee referral. Typically the cost per hire is lower, applicant quality is higher, and the attrition rate is reduced. This is mainly because employees are more likely to recommend candidates who emulate their work ethic. Also, most employees want to maintain a good working relationship with their employer who will not promote those individuals lacking in job performance.

There are benefits and disadvantages of using employee referral. With few exceptions, it tends to replicate the makeup of the current workforce. This should be considered if the manager is seeking diversity within the department. Keep in mind that employee referral is a valuable tool if the department has happy, motivated employees. Conversely, this is not true if the current employee base is disgruntled.

Depending on the environment, informal referral programs (no incentive offered) can work effectively. A rule of thumb applies: when the program is first introduced, employees will make referrals; however, as is generally the case, interest declines over time and management will constantly need to keep reminding employees to refer. Methods may include posters, pep talks at staff meetings, and talking it up informally. Generally, when an employee starts a new job the excitement level is high. Managers need to use this to their advantage by promoting the employee referral program during new employee orientation. Ask new hires to submit the name of a candidate they would like to refer.

Guidelines for incentive-based employee referrals:

- Design and award incentives that match the appropriate level of the position. Incentives are generally money, prizes, and gift certificates. One suggestion would be to work with the human resource department to develop a reasonable and obtainable award program by basing the incentive on cost per hire savings. Solicit incentive ideas through an employee task force—what do they feel is fair compensation?
- Immediately reward the employee. Do not tie the reward into retention rates; the employee exercises no control over the tenure of referred workers. Make the payment effective within 30 days. If payment is immediate, it will have a positive ripple effect throughout the department by increasing morale and encouraging more referrals.
- Keep interest high by occasionally changing various incentive elements. Decrease program stagnation by changing awards or prizes, change the time periods for recruitment, and offer higher incentives for positions that are difficult to recruit for.
- Activate the program only during peak need periods. Most organizations with peak recruitment needs find that employee referral is effective if used for a specific period of time. Adjust the award program by offering a special or additional prize during times with high recruitment needs.
- Keep it simple. If there is a question as to whether or not an employee is eligible for an incentive, decide in favor of the employee. If not in favor of the employee, this will work to the disadvantage of the manager by ultimately lowering morale and adversely effecting response rates.

Staffing Alternatives

It has become increasingly apparent that the traditional method of meeting staffing needs may not have a place in today's work environment. Full time permanent positions are becoming an anachronism in the current workforce. Many facilities are offering staffing alternatives to attract qualified technologists, including the following:

- Part time. Employees usually work less than the traditional 40 hour work week, generally 30 hours or less.
- Job sharing. Dividing 1 full time job into 2 part time positions, with both employees sharing responsibilities.
- Flex time. Permits employees to determine the times of day they work, most often around prime time when the majority of employees are on the job. This arrangement usually does not find favor in most healthcare institutions, as patient care is a service required 24 hours per day, 7 days per week, 365 days per year.
- Peak time scheduling. A concept borrowed from the service industry—scheduling part time coverage during peak need times (Friday and Saturday night emergency department duty). This schedule has appeal for those workers that wish to work less time (<20 hours) than traditional part time employees.
- Compressed work schedule. Scheduling full time hours outside of the traditional 8 hour, 5 day work week. Examples are 4, 10 hour days each week or 3, 12 hour days.
- Employer sponsored daycare that matches work hours.

Any one of these staffing alternatives holds an appeal for those candidates that might not have otherwise considered the organization for employment. These candidates may be one of the following labor market groups:

- Older/retired workers, who desire more leisure time for family and travel. They generally have a source of income which they wish to supplement.
- Students who need to work around their school schedule.
- Dual career couples and single parents, who wish to balance work and family obligations.

These alternative staffing methods may provide imaging managers, especially those confronted with staffing challenges, an alternative to recruiting full time technologists. This model allows for staffing flexibility, while offering work schedules that allow nontraditional employees to meet their lifestyle needs.

Filling the Pool

The timeline associated with the ongoing process of recruitment is increasing. Vacant imaging technologist positions that in the past may have taken 1 to 2 weeks to fill may now exceed a month. The search for filling vacancies in specialized modalities (nuclear medicine, sonography, mammography, etc) can go on for much longer.

Do not wait until an opening occurs to begin recruitment. Give consideration to creating a pool of qualified applicants. The imaging manager can begin by utilizing low key advertising that appeals to technologists who are currently employed and pleased with their current situation. Avoid building the pool by appealing to the unemployed individual—they probably will not wait until an opportunity exists in the organization, but most likely accept the first offer of employment elsewhere.

One way to maintain a high level of interest in a department is to stay in touch with the candidates through some type of follow up. Structure a timeline (monthly or quarterly) and contact the pool by either personalized correspondence (include the organization's newsletter) and direct telephone calls to update them on their status. This small effort can help through a recruitment downturn.

Conclusion

For an imaging manager to achieve success in a competitive labor market, honesty must be first and foremost. An imaging manager can set realistic expectations with the following:

- Present both the positive and negative aspects of employment. If the work is hard, hours are long, shift work is available, be up front. If the job has challenges, but opportunities for career growth and advancement exist, be equally vocal. Provide an honest assessment of what the job entails.
- Provide a tour of the department. Pair up the newly hired employee with a seasoned technologist; this should allow the candidate a real perspective of what the job entails.
- Be knowledgeable of the benefits that the organization can deliver. Do not promise what may not come true.

Recruitment is one of the most exciting and challenging components of running a modern imaging facility. If radiology is unable to attract and recruit top employees to meet staffing needs, this all important segment of the healthcare delivery system will be unable to provide a standard of care that is recognized universally as the best and will ultimately fail, as it is the highly trained and motivated employee that constitutes the bedrock of all healthcare organizations.

References

1. Olivi P. Crystal ball predictions. *Radiol Manage* 2004;26:15–16.

2. American Society of Radiologic Technologists. R.T. Recruitment and retention tool kit. Available at: http://asrt.org/content/RecruitmentandRetention/RecruitmentTools/Recruitment_Strategies.aspx. Accessed October 29, 2006.

3. Bureau of Labor Statistics, U.S. Department of Labor. *Employment Outlook: 2000–10. Occupational Employment Projections to 2010. Monthly Labor Review.* Washington, DC: U.S. Department of Labor; 2001.

4. Collins SK, Collins KS. Employee retention: an issue of survival in healthcare. *Radiol Manage* 2004;26:52–55.

5. Stubbington V, PHR, Senior Human Resources Representative, Scott & White, Temple, TX. Interview conducted October 27, 2006.

Bibliography

Kichline D. On the auction block [RT image]. November 29, 2004. Available at: http://www.rt-image.com/content. Accessed October 29, 2006.

Mornell P. *45 Effective Ways For Hiring Smart!* Berkeley, CA: Ten Speed Press; 1998.

Ryan MJ. The predictable swarm: staying on top of radiology's cyclical staffing "bug". *Radiol Manage* 2005;27:14–29.

Wolski C. 4 Ways to staff up. *Decis Imaging Econ* 2003;16:42–45.

Wolski C. Recruiting technologists: building a ladder to retention. *Decis Imaging Econ* 2004;17:35–44.

Chapter 5

Developing a Recruitment Strategy, Plan, and Timeline

Kathy Tabor McEwan and Martha Munhall

> *Developing a recruitment strategy for short range needs, based on the existing workforce, and long range needs, based on growth, will prepare the organization to fill all types of staff vacancies. Once a strategy has been developed, a plan and timeline will provide the detail for the tactical work to be done, immediately and on an ongoing basis.*

Imaging administrators who work with full time human resource personnel can rely on those professionals to help devise a recruitment strategy and plan, advise on and maintain databases of recruitment tools, measure the tools' effectiveness, and carry out many of the tasks on the plan, as described in this chapter. Yet even in the largest organizations, administrators may find themselves responsible for devising the department specific strategy and plan, identifying industry specific resources, cohosting booths at job fairs, volunteering to speak at relevant meetings, keeping the human resource department informed about pending openings and industry trends, and maintaining the departmental recruitment budget. Managers in smaller facilities, on the other hand, will find themselves responsible for nearly all aspects of recruiting but can enlist the help of staff members who may welcome the variety and challenge of putting together an open house, for example, or researching online recruiting resources.

Developing the Recruitment Strategy

The workforce plan, described in Chapter 2, is the starting point for most recruitment efforts. It provides data on the imaging facility's short and long range workforce needs, which are the drivers for the recruitment effort. In both large and small organizations, a recruitment strategy provides a focus for this effort. It is a concise statement that describes in general terms how recruitment will be carried out to achieve the desired workforce outcome. A facility may have a strategy related to its long range recruitment and others that guide each short range hiring. Strategies change as new tools are developed, results fail to achieve targets, and workforce needs change.

For example, ABC Imaging Associates has a workforce plan that seeks to recruit, develop, and promote a diverse mix of experienced professionals and recent college graduates. From this, the imaging administrator devises several recruitment strategies. The facility's long range college recruitment strategy is to hire diverse, top quality graduates in a cost effective, efficient manner. After a key staff member gives a brief notice of resignation, the short range recruitment strategy is to hire an experienced professional who would need minimal training and to use tools that historically have shown the shortest time-to-hire.

Criteria Underlying a Recruitment Plan and Timeline

The recruitment plan and its related timeline describe how the strategy will be carried out. In devising a plan, Diane Arthur, author of *The Employee Recruitment and Retention Handbook*, suggests answering these 4 questions[1]:

1. How much money is available to achieve the recruitment strategy?
2. How quickly must the opening(s) be filled?
3. How wide must the candidate pool be?
4. Is the position exempt or nonexempt?

Once the imaging administrator has established the answers, he or she can evaluate the available recruitment tools, many of which have been described in Chapter 4. The goal is to identify the tools that best meet the criteria established by these questions.

Budget as a Factor

The direct cost for using various recruitment tools can vary from $0 (posting jobs on the facility's Web site) to $30,000 or more (using a recruiting agency). Add on the indirect costs, such as the manager's time spent interviewing, and the applicant costs, such as travel reimbursement, and the cost of recruiting employees can take a big bite out of a facility's budget.

Setting an effective recruitment budget is not easy, and it is not "one size fits all." However, 2 sets of data, taken from the facility's recruitment history, can contribute significantly to the imaging administrator's ability to set an appropriate budget.

The first data set is called the cost-per-hire. Whereas human resource professionals in large organizations calculate cost-per-hire by using direct, indirect, and candidate costs,[2] the complexity of this calculation makes it less useful for smaller organizations or for operational managers carrying out human resource functions. Nevertheless, a simpler cost-per-hire calculation based on direct costs can be useful.

There are 2 ways to present cost-per-hire data.[3] The first is as overall spending, usually subdivided by exempt and nonexempt hires. To calculate these data, divide the total spent in direct costs on recruiting exempt employees over a specified time period (eg, a month) by the number of exempt employees hired. Repeat the calculation for nonexempt employees. For example, if an imaging center spent $26,500 in a month to recruit 4 exempt employees and $1500 to hire 2 nonexempt staff members, the cost-per-hire would be $6625 for exempt and $750 for nonexempt. If the imaging administrator's short range recruitment plan called for hiring 2 exempt and 1 nonexempt employees within the next month, the budget for recruitment tools (direct costs) could be set at about $14,000 [($6625 × 2) + $750].

The second form of average cost-per-hire is calculated for each type of recruitment tool used. Table 5.1 shows the cost-per-hire by tool for a hypothetical multisite radiation oncology practice.

Table 5.1 also provides an example of the second data set useful in setting an appropriate budget and later in building the plan. That is the percentage of total hires by recruitment tool, also known as the source cost analysis. This is calculated by dividing the number of new employees recruited with a specific tool by the total number of new employees for the period. The percentage is an indicator of effectiveness and, therefore, of the tools most likely to find similar new employees in the future. Because some tools are more useful in identifying exempt employees than nonexempt staff, the imaging administrator may want to calculate a separate percentage of total hire for the 2 categories.

Table 5.1 Average Cost-per-Hire by Recruitment Tool for ABC Radiology Associates

Tool	Amount Spent ÷	No. of Recruits =	Average Cost-per-Hire	No. of Recruits per Tool	Percentage of Total Hires
Print advertising	$18,250	15	$1217	4	26.7
Internet	7200	15	480	3	20
Recruiting agency	110,000	15	7333	4	27
Employee referral	4000	15	267	2	13.3
College recruiting	12,000	15	800	2	13.3

Timing as a Factor

Even a well thought out staffing plan cannot anticipate every vacancy, and many of these unanticipated vacancies will need to be filled promptly. Filling vacancies with temporary staff can be both expensive and difficult for permanent staff. Temporary staff members usually need time to become acclimated to the equipment, office procedures, and the culture. Leaving vacancies unfilled, on the other hand, creates stress among the permanent staff and can lower morale. They must work harder and longer just to maintain the same level of service.

Occasionally, the imaging administrator may have substantial lead time before a position must be filled (eg, when plans for an additional office site are announced). In addition, facilities with large staffs and/or substantial turnover will want to carry out ongoing recruitment in anticipation of future openings.

All of these elements influence the timing of the recruitment effort and the selection of recruitment tools. In general, the effectiveness of these tools can be viewed as appropriate for either short range or long range recruiting (see Sidebar 5.1).

These are general guidelines. By reviewing the facility's recruitment history, the imaging administrator can estimate the actual time-to-hire for each tool. Much like the basic cost-to-hire analysis, time-to-hire data are generated by a simple calculation. For each tool used, divide the total days needed to hire over a specified time period (eg, a month) by the number of employees hired. For example, at a hypothetical

---

SIDEBAR 5.1: Selecting Appropriate Recruitment Tools

Short Range

- Newspaper advertisement
- Radio advertisement
- Internet advertisement
- Reviewing past resumes on file
- Internal job posting
- Recruiting agency

Long Range

- Open house
- Job fair
- College recruiting
- Employee referral
- Billboards
- Professional journal advertisement

---

imaging center, 3 employees were hired during May, all of whom applied in response to newspaper advertisements. The length of time from appearance of the advertisement to acceptance was 18 working days for the first position, 23 for the second, and 35 for the third. At this imaging center, the time-to-hire for newspapers would be 25 days [(18 + 23 + 35) ÷ 3].

Candidate Pool Size as a Factor

A recruitment plan needs to take into account how many applications must be reviewed to fill a position with the right candidate and in a timely fashion. Issues that affect pool size include:

- Position specialization: The more highly specialized the position, the larger the pool needs to be in order to find someone with the necessary qualifications.
- Position specification: The less clearly a position's needs are specified, the greater the pool must be.
- Labor market: A tight labor market reduces the number of candidates responding to a given recruitment tool and tightens the competition for candidates, presenting them with multiple offers to consider. A larger pool gives an employer an alternative if the first choice candidate accepts another offer.

Trend analysis used in preparing the facility's workforce plan can be useful in assessing the candidate pool size, particularly for long range recruiting (see Chapter 2). If the demand for imaging technologists grows as expected and enrollment in training programs declines, demand for skilled professionals will be intense. A facility's long range recruitment plan may need to include a wide range of tools, aggressively applied, to meet projected needs.

As with so many activities, the Internet has had a major impact on recruitment, including significantly increasing the number of resumes most employers receive. Simply posting jobs on the organization's Web site can result in many more resumes than any other recruitment tool. The imaging administrator should review the facility's recruitment history to determine which of the other tools have produced the largest response. Depending on the region and type of job, tools that tend to offer large candidate pools include newspaper and radio advertisements and recruiting agencies.

Exempt Status as a Factor

As detailed in Chapter 7, federal law identifies positions as exempt (ie, exempt from overtime) and nonexempt. Exempt positions include those in management and professional salaried categories, whereas nonexempt generally refers to hourly workers. Some recruitment tools are more effective at reaching candidates for nonexempt than for exempt positions, including newspaper and radio advertising, employee referrals, employment agencies, and government agencies (eg, state employment office). Tools that generally reach candidates for exempt positions include professional journal advertising, direct mail, executive search firms, campus recruiting, and job fairs.[1] In considering which Internet job sites to use, the imaging administrator should pay particular attention to the types of candidates the site is designed to attract, which can be determined by visiting the sites or consulting *Weddle's Guide to Employment Web Sites*.[4]

Developing the Short Range Recruitment Plan and Timeline

As soon as an employee gives notice of his or her intention to leave, the imaging administrator should start recruiting. This process should begin with a recruitment plan, using the following steps and based on the analysis of the 4 factors previously discussed.

1. Collect, if necessary, a revised copy of the job description and prioritize the position in light of other recruitment needs.
2. Set the budget for direct costs and for candidate costs, if relevant.
3. Set a target date for hiring the new employee.
4. Select recruitment tools based on the 4 factors.
5. Develop a timeline, working back from the target hire date, and incorporating timelines related to advertising or other deadlines.
6. Monitor effectiveness; if the caliber or number of candidates is inadequate, reevaluate tool selection and consider alternatives.
7. Measure responses to each tool, time-to-hire, and cost-to-hire to guide future recruitment efforts.

A sample short range recruitment plan for a hypothetical imaging facility is provided in Box 5.1.

Developing the Long Range Recruitment Plan and Timeline

Recruitment is not a phase; it is not something to be done just when a vacancy occurs. Recruitment is an ongoing process that needs to be monitored and updated as the workforce and the facility's needs change.

Box 5.1 Sample Short Range Recruitment Plan

Position: Receptionist-scheduler (nonexempt, full time)

Strategy: To hire a bilingual individual with medical front office experience using tools with low time-to-hire and direct cost-to-hire

Target date to hire: 20 days from notification date

Budget: $2200 (direct costs)

Timeline:
Week 1
- Review resumes on file from previous receptionist opening and reinterview any likely candidates by telephone for availability, interest
- Post job on facility's Web site and employee bulletin board
- Post job on Hispanic job site (eg, www.empleosCB.com)
- Submit job advertisement to local Hispanic and daily English language newspapers

Week 2
- Review resumes received to date
- Conduct preliminary telephone interview(s)
- Repeat newspaper advertisements

Week 3
- Conduct preliminary telephone interview(s) from additional candidates
- Conduct face-to-face interviews with first choice candidates
- Check references for finalist(s)

Week 4
- Conduct second face-to-face interview with finalist(s)
- Make offer
- Notify rejected candidates of decision

As previously noted, the recruitment plan evolves from the strategic plan. In the broadest sense, everything about the facility can contribute to the success of recruitment efforts, particularly with regard to long range recruitment. The organization's reputation as a clinical research site or a provider of comprehensive radiation oncology services, for example, can attract high quality professionals. A well designed, informative Web site can give potential employees their first impressions of the facility.

With this broader context in mind, the imaging administrator can devise an annual long range recruitment plan that will support the strategic plan by carrying out the following steps:

Box 5.2 Sample Long Range Recruitment Plan for Imaging Technologists

Strategy: Recruit a diverse mix of new college graduates and experienced professionals to fulfill requirements to provide imaging technology services

Plan Overview: In the facility's completely digital imaging department, a highly skilled workforce is needed to sustain high levels of quality and patient care, while continuing to meet the demands for increased efficiencies. To continue to recruit and sustain a more highly skilled workforce, 3 initiatives are being implemented: (1) aggressive recruitment of technologists; (2) competency based training of staff technologists; and (3) quality program for image management. This document focuses on the recruitment initiative.

Budget (fiscal year starting in October): $32,000 (direct costs)

Timeline:

Quarter 1 (October–December)

- Participate in career fairs at selected colleges with imaging technologist degree programs (selection based on previous success in identifying candidates, program size)
- Run general display advertisement in the journal of the American Society of Radiologic Technologists (ASRT)
- Hold open house to mark Sonographer Awareness Month (October) and National Radiologic Technology Week (early November)
- Meet with guidance counselor of local high school with healthcare career program to discuss possible scholarship, other opportunities to encourage students to pursue further education in imaging technology
- Review facility's Web site and update information about career opportunities, including imaging technology

Quarter 2 (January–March)

- Volunteer to speak at state imaging technology society meeting
- Follow up on college visits with newsletter/brochure mailing to all contacts
- Run general display advertisement in ASRT' journal and follow up with any inquiries from previous advertisements
- Speak to class of students in local high school healthcare career program about imaging technology and other imaging careers; offer tour to interested students

Quarter 3 (April–June)

- Participate in Latin American Association Career Expo (May)
- Participate in career fair at selected colleges with imaging technologist degree programs that graduate in August/September (selection based on previous success in identifying candidates, program size)
- Follow up on Fall college visits and Spring career expo with newsletter/brochure mailing to all contacts
- Run general display advertisement in ASRT journal and follow up with any inquiries from previous advertisements

Quarter 4 (July–September)

- Participate in National Society for Hispanic Professionals Job Fair (September)
- Participate in ASRT annual conference (September) by conducting a workshop and having a recruitment booth
- Promote forthcoming open house by mailing flyers to local high school with healthcare career program, contacts from Fall and Spring college visits and job fairs, and members of the state imaging technology society
- Follow up with any inquiries from journal advertisements

1. Identify long range staffing needs and prioritize the various positions.
2. Set a budget.
3. Set monthly recruitment goals.
4. Identify recruitment tools that are best suited to the budget, staffing needs, and longer range horizon.
5. Anticipate and plan for seasonal cycles related to specific tools, staffing projects, and candidate availability (eg, college graduations).
6. If advertising is being planned, identify the specific media and devise timelines to create an advertising schedule.
7. Build strategic alliances with local community colleges, chapters of professional organizations, recruitment agencies, ethnic groups and organizations, and universities.
8. If job fairs and college recruitment are planned, collect information and add key dates to timeline.
9. If an employee referral program is planned, establish guidelines and incentives, develop a communication plan, and add key dates to the timeline.
10. Measure the effectiveness of each tool, compiling cost-to-hire, time-to-hire, and response rate, whenever possible.

Box 5.2 shows an example of a basic long range recruitment plan, which is focused on imaging technology, for a large multisite imaging center. Refer to Chapter 4 for details about how to effectively use each recruitment tool.

Conclusion

A properly designed and communicated recruitment strategy and its related plan are worth the investment of time and effort. They help management focus on the facility's immediate needs, while preparing for future growth and long term workforce needs. A well devised plan will help control recruitment costs and ensure that funds are spent efficiently and effectively, lessen the need for costly temporary staffing, lessen the stress on permanent employees who must take on additional tasks while a position remains unfilled, contribute to achieving organizational goals, and help ensure long term stability.

References

1. Arthur D. *The Employee Recruitment and Retention Handbook.* New York, NY: American Management Association; 2001.

2. Brown J. Calculating cost per hire. International Public Management Association for Human Resources. Available at: http://www.ipma-hr.org/content.cfm?pageid=288. Accessed February 12, 2008.

3. Falcone P. *The Hiring and Firing Question and Answer Book.* New York, NY: American Management Association; 2002.

4. Weddle P. *Weddle's 2007/8 Guide to Employment Web Sites.* 8th ed. Stamford, CT: Weddles; 2007.

Chapter 6

Talent Selection

Winnie Grieshaber

Finding the right candidates to fill openings within the organization is one of the most important functions of a manager. Open positions result when someone leaves the organization or the workload increases. In an attempt to eliminate the gap between the time when a need is identified and the position is filled, managers often fill vacancies quickly, with the wrong candidates. In healthcare organizations, supervisors who have received very little interviewing training often conduct interviews. Imaging administrators need to understand that training and preparation are vital for a successful selection process. A quality selection process requires a great deal of time and effort, but the results are worth the effort. With the right team in place, a manager is able to spend time and resources on other issues.

The talent selection process begins with a review of the job description for the position. As jobs change over time, this review also presents a good opportunity to update the job description. (See Chapter 3 for more information on building job descriptions). Box 6.1 offers guidance on defining requirements during this process. Throughout the resume review and interview process, human resource staff and/or the imaging administrator should review the qualifications of potential candidates to determine if they meet the minimum requirements as outlined in the job description and remove those who do not meet these qualifications from the candidate pool.

Interviewing

Recruitment will provide resumes of potential candidates for any open position. In many organizations, human resource staff will perform the initial screening. In other facilities, the imaging administrator may be responsible for all tasks related to hiring.

A preliminary telephone interview with the candidate should provide additional detailed information beyond that given in the resume. This initial conversation should be brief. It is an opportunity to provide more information about the open position to the candidate, including clarification of job requirements and performance expectations. The candidate should verify his or her ability to fulfill the job requirements and be able to ask questions about the position. After verifying the candidate's continued interest in the position and general suitability, the imaging administrator can make an appointment for a more in depth personal or second phone interview.

Box 6.1 Requirements of the Position

- Specific knowledge and skills required
- Background and experience required
- Formal education required
- Necessary familiarity with specific equipment or processes
- Job duties, including what is expected in the way of quality and output
- Responsibility for supervision of others, if applicable
- Responsibility for the safety of others, if applicable
- Potential loss due to error
- Confidentiality requirements
- Contacts and relationships with others (customers, vendors, the public, etc)
- Physical demands (lifting, pushing, pulling, and the weights involved)
- Visual, auditory, and other sensory requirements
- Potential stressors (pace, pressures, etc)
- Closeness of supervision or relative independence of the position
- Working conditions (hours, locations, hazards, travel, etc)
- Compensation and benefits
- Future potential

Source: Kroken P, Richardson E, Stockburger W, eds. *Communication & Information Management in Radiology.* Sudbury, MA: American Healthcare Radiology Administrators; 2007.

Interview can be defined as a directed, goal oriented conversation to determine the suitability of a candidate or applicant for a specific position. The interviewing process should be established within an organization and within the individual department. As noted, many organizations depend on the human resource staff to do the preliminary work. Then the hiring manager is given a list of qualified candidates and their resumes and other information to review before the interviews.

Most facilities have guidelines for the interview process. Some organizations use a team to conduct interviews, whereas others choose to let one person do all the interviewing for a given position. This person could be the human resource director or the lead person in the modality that has the open position. Becoming familiar with these guidelines will help managers be more comfortable with the process.

Training in interviewing techniques is essential. The imaging administrator needs to become comfortable with whatever process the organization has chosen to use. Interviewers are expected to know and understand the implications of employment laws and how these laws protect both the candidates and the interviewers (see Chapter 1). They should understand how to score and evaluate answers given by applicants and the value of interpreting nonverbal communication behaviors, such as posture and eye contact. See Sidebar 6.1 for more on body language.

As part of the interview process, pre-employment testing often proves beneficial. Applicants can be asked to perform tasks that are included in the job description.

Body language is a term used for components of communication that include body move-
ments or gestures that can be used with spoken words or in lieu of them. Body language is
driven by culture; what is perceived as pleasant in one culture may be perceived as obscene
in another. For example, in the United States and Canada, looking at one's watch while listening to someone conveys impatience or unwillingness to really listen to the other person. Also,
standing with arms across the chest can convey a defensive posture, whereas arms by the
side can convey receptivity. Showing palms to a listener means openness; the opposite ges-
ture of closed palms can be interpreted as hiding something. Sitting so a leg or knee points
to a person means interest in that person, whereas turning away from a person means one
does not want to talk to the individual. A physical impairment, such as an inability to move
one's arm because of a stroke, may also affect a person's body language.

Source: Kroken P, Richardson E, Stockburger W, eds. *Communication & Information Management in Radiology.* Sudbury,
MA: American Healthcare Radiology Administrators; 2007.

Some facilities conduct a cognitive skills test, when appropriate. All testing needs to
be job related and should be administered to all applicants for a given position.

Interviewing Methods

Ideally, effective interviewing will combine 2 or more of the different types of
interviews. Ultimately, however, these assessment tools are not a substitute for
managerial judgments.

Unstructured or Informal Interviewing Techniques

The unstructured or informal interview consists of a loose set of questions, which
may vary from interview to interview. The factors evaluated by the interview are
implicit and vary across candidates. Questions are not necessarily job related, and
there is no system or guide for evaluating the interview results. This type of interview places the manager at greatest risk of grievances. The informal interview is the
most susceptible to complaints. When there is inconsistency with questions and
poor or nonexistent documentation about each applicant, the interviewer and the
organization are vulnerable to legal actions.

Structured Interviewing Technique

The structured interview consists of a specific series of questions and is designed to
obtain meaningful information about a candidate's ability to perform the job. The
factors evaluated are explicit, based on analysis, and are the same for each candidate.
All questions are job related, but the same questions are asked of each candidate for
the same vacancy. There is a predetermined system for evaluating interview results.

The structured interview is not without faults. Applicants can obtain questions and
their answers in advance from a variety of sources. Questions are often recycled for

a wide variety of related jobs. This type of interview evaluates the applicants on their previous work experiences as opposed to their ability to apply their knowledge and experience to the performance of the new job. Furthermore, many applicants can "talk the talk." That person may not be the top performer, but rather, the most successful "impression manager" and the most prepared applicant. In such instances, conducting the second interview in several settings may be a way to get prepared applicants out of their comfort zone. Carrying out the interview in a different office or the employee lounge, while walking on a tour through the department, or even over lunch in the cafeteria with a third party present may reveal behaviors and details these carefully prepared candidates would not otherwise disclose.

Performance Based Interviewing Technique

The performance based interview contains elements that are specific to the vacancy, facility issues, and work culture. This technique is similar but superior to the structured interview. Applicants are asked to perform tasks and resolve problems that would be typical of the new job (ie, a candidate applying for a position as a computed tomography [CT] technologist is asked to perform an actual CT examination, under supervision). This type of interview can be quickly developed because the questions come directly from the job tasks. They have a long shelf life because they can be easily modified. The only way applicants can successfully answer all the questions is if they can truly perform all aspects of the job and its required tasks, demonstrating their talented skill set as a testament to knowing and understanding the position for which they are applying.

Case Based Interviewing Technique

The case based interview technique is similar to performance based interviews except that the candidate is asked to describe how he or she would respond in a hypothetical situation, rather than actually performing an activity. If the candidate is encouraged to "think out loud" in deciding what to do, the interviewer can gain insight into the candidate's analytic and decision making skills. This technique can also provide a mechanism for evaluating the candidate's judgment, ability to troubleshoot, and follow through. Each candidate is given the same situation(s), allowing for comparison of responses. The disadvantage of case based interviewing lies in its hypothetical nature. No matter how likely the scenario, the candidate's answer in most instances reflects how he or she would want to respond (or what the candidate thinks the employer wants for a response).

Behavioral Interviewing Technique

If one accepts that past performance is an accurate guide to future job performance, the behavioral interview provides the most useful information. This type of interview focuses on competencies drawn from the job description and asks the candidate to describe, in detail, how he or she carried out a project or responded in a situation. Candidates are asked to describe a situation, what action they took, and what the results were. Often, candidates are free to select examples from not only employment, but also volunteer or school experience, so the technique can be used with new graduates as well as seasoned professionals. Questions may ask about negative or positive situations. For example:

- Describe a specific problem you solved for a previous supervisor or in a similar setting. How did you approach the problem? What resources did you use? What was the outcome?
- Tell me about a project you were responsible for. What was the goal? How did you proceed? Was it completed on time? What was the result?

The first question evaluates candidates' problem solving and decision making skills and highlights their ability to marshal and manage resources. The second set of questions highlights candidates' planning and organizational skills, commitment to task, and goal achievement.

Devising behavioral questions that relate to a job's competencies is somewhat more difficult than asking, "What did you like about your last position?" The interview may take longer, depending on the examples the candidate gives, but the information provided is very helpful in comparing and contrasting candidates.

What to Avoid

Interviewers must be constantly aware of questions or comments that could be taken as discriminatory and may not ask about a candidate's marital status, number of children, race, nationality, religion, or age. Box 6.2 provides an example of questions that are legal and illegal to ask during an interview. Effective human resource department procedures should take most of the burden, but interviewers should be familiar with the state and federal regulations surrounding discrimination and hiring practices. (See Chapter 1 for more information on the impact of employment law on human resource practice.)

Asking questions about the identity of the applicant's nearest relative, or next of kin, can be construed as probing into the existence of spouse or family and should be avoided until the applicant is actually employed. Even if an applicant has willingly revealed marriage on a resume, the interviewer is not permitted to ask what the spouse does for a living or ask a woman for her maiden name because this could be interpreted as probing for clues to national origin.

Applicants cannot be asked about home or automobile ownership because to do so can be interpreted as seeking a test of affluence. Credit information is another area of privileged information, so questions about garnished wages or outstanding loans must be avoided. The interviewer can ask about a driver's license if driving is a bona fide occupational qualification.

Box 6.2 Legal and Illegal Questions

Although some of the following questions may have been asked on the application form, the interviewer should know which questions asked during an interview may cause a liability for the company.

Citizenship:

Legal: *If you are a not a US citizen, have you the right to remain permanently in the United States?*

Illegal: *Of what country are you a citizen? Are you, your spouse, or parents naturalized or native-born US citizens? What date did you acquire citizenship?*

National Origin:

Legal: *What languages do you speak, read, or write?*

Illegal: *What is your nationality, lineage, national origin, or descent? What languages do you use, or what is your native tongue?*

Character:

Legal: *Have you ever been convicted of any crime? If so, when, where, and what is the disposition of the case?*

Illegal: *Have you ever been arrested?*

Notice in Case of Emergency:

Legal: *What is the name and address of the person to notify in case of an emergency?*

Illegal: *What is the relationship of the person to be notified?*

Experience:

Legal: *What is your military experience in the US Armed Forces?*

Illegal: *Please produce your discharge papers (before employment).*

Age:

Legal: *Can you submit proof of age, if necessary for a work permit, after actual employment? Are you under the age of 18?*

Illegal: *May I see your birth certificate (before employment)?*

Organizational Affiliations:

Legal: *Are you a member of any clubs, organizations, professional associations, or other associations, excluding any organization whose name would indicate race, religion, national origin, or ancestry of its members?*

Illegal: *Are you a member of any clubs, organizations, professional associations, or other associations whose name would indicate race, religion, national origin, or ancestry of its members?*

Religion:

Legal: *Are you willing and able to work shifts and workdays required by the job?*

Illegal: *Anything about religion, period.*

Sources: McConnell C. *The Effective Health Care Supervisor,* 5th ed. Sudbury, MA: Jones and Bartlett Publishers; 2003.

California State Personnel Board. Guidelines for developing and conducting structured hiring interviews. Available at: http://www.spb.ca.gov/tvc/intguide.htm. Accessed September 20, 2004.

An interviewer may not directly ask any applicant's height or weight unless there is a specific job related requirement that is uniformly applied to all applicants. Educational levels that are bona fide occupational qualifications can be discussed.

Conducting the Interview

During the interview, the goal is for the interviewer and the candidate to learn as much as possible about each other to determine a good fit for the organization. Before beginning, the interviewer should follow several steps to prepare:

- Determine who is going to be responsible for interviewing candidates. A panel or group can be more effective for the process because of the potential of capturing information that a single person could miss.
- Prepare a list of questions to ask. Carefully construct questions that will provide as much information about the candidate as possible. Focus on open-ended questions and use closed-ended (yes/no) sparingly or avoid them altogether. Interviewers should know which questions to avoid during the process, as previously noted.
- Review the resumes and other documents on all qualified candidates. Each person responsible for interviewing should be provided with a resume for each candidate and have an opportunity to review it before the interview.
- Determine how to score the responses from each candidate.

The interviewer should be knowledgeable about the open position and the facility's policies to be able to discuss them during the interview. The predetermined questions should be asked in the same order for each candidate.

Setting

The interview should take place in an area that is private, quiet, and relatively comfortable, where interruptions can be avoided. The ability to learn about the applicant is severely impaired by interruptions, which can be unsettling to the applicant as well. Conducting an interview requires patience on the part of the manager. During the first few critical minutes of an interview, the applicant should be given time to relax, with general conversation in language appropriate to the apparent level of education. The process should be explained to the applicant so he or she will know what to expect. If taking notes, the interviewer should assure the applicant that the note taking is a memory aid and will assist in making an objective and informed decision.

Question Structure

Asking the right questions, listening carefully to the answers, and then interpreting them accurately are fundamental to effective hiring. No matter what type of interview technique is being used, questions should primarily be open-ended to encourage applicants to talk and give more complete responses. Open-ended questions help achieve the optimum balance between the amount of talking the interviewer should do (about 20%) compared to the amount of talking the applicant should do (about 80%).[1] Open-ended questions usually begin with words like *how*, *why*, *describe*, *tell me*, and *in what way*. These questions solicit views, opinions, thoughts, and feelings as well as stimulating a 2-way interaction (Box 6.3). The applicant should be given time to formulate a response. Learning as much as possible about the applicant in a limited amount of time is accomplished by listening to the person talk.

Box 6.3 Sample Interview Questions

Personal

1. Please tell me about yourself.
2. Why are you interested in joining our organization?
3. Why do you feel qualified for this job?
4. What skills and abilities do you possess that will help you succeed in this position?
5. What do you see as your greatest challenge when starting a new position?

Work experience

6. What prior work experience do you have?
7. How does it relate to this position?
8. What were your job responsibilities?
9. What were your accomplishments?
10. What would your last 2 employers/supervisors say about you as an employee, either good or bad?
11. Why did you decide to concentrate on or specialize in [particular area]?
12. How did you go about [learning a job, solving a problem, organizing a project]?

Education

13. How would you describe your education?
14. Have you had any special training for [qualification factor]?
15. Do you hold certifications in any areas?

Communication and interpersonal skills

16. What has your relationship with coworkers been like?
17. Have you ever had a job related crisis?
18. How did you handle it?
19. Describe a time when you were able to facilitate an exchange of unpleasant information.
20. Giving respect is a real challenge. When did you find it difficult to give respect to a person in a higher position and what did you do?
21. Give an example when you had to adapt your communication style in order to build your professional network.
22. For you, what are some of the pros and cons of working on a team project?
23. Who was the most difficult person you have ever dealt with, and how did you respond?

Box 6.3 (Continued)

Career goals and objectives

24. What are your short range goals and objectives?
25. What are your long range goals and objective?
26. What motivates you to put forth your greatest effort?
27. What are your strongest points?
28. Are there areas of weakness that we should know about?

Hypothetical questions

29. What do you see as the major objective of this job?
30. When comparing this facility to others, what factors are important to you other than salary?
31. What do you think you can contribute to this department?
32. How did you find out about our opportunity ?

Performance of task

Please demonstrate or explain how you perform [job specific task]:

33._____
34._____
35._____
36._____

Reading over the job description, are there any tasks that you cannot fulfill?

If so, what tasks are they and why can you not perform them?

Would you like to add additional information for us to consider when evaluating you for this position?

Source: Weemploy.com. Interviewing techniques. Available at: http://www.weemploy.com/interviewing.htm. Accessed September 20, 2004.

During the interview, the interviewer should look for limitations (ie, reasons the applicant is not right for the job). If a limitation exists, the interviewer needs to project what impact it will have on job performance. It can be less difficult to discover the applicant's positive or strong points than to discover his or her weaknesses because most applicants concentrate on their strengths. Again, asking open-ended questions is the most effective means to determine limitations. When interviewers seem to accept failings, applicants are more likely to reveal their true limitations, so asking questions that assume limitations are acceptable may lead to these revelations (eg, "Which areas of this job do you think will be the most difficult?").

For a fair and accurate appraisal, the interviewer should press for specifics during the interview. Most applicants speak in generalities that are open to a variety of interpretations. Specifics are more factual than generalities and enable interviewers to separate an applicant's actual behavior from his or her claims about behavior. Any notes the interviewer makes should be made on a separate paper or form, not the resume or application; something as simple as circling a graduation date could indicate a reference to age. Notes should relate only to the job for which the candidate is applying. If a report of the interview must be kept, the manager should write it immediately after the meeting while the conversation is still fresh.

Subsequent Interviews

At the close of the interview, the candidate should be thanked for his or her interest in the position and given some indication of impending follow up (ie, "We will call you no later than next Tuesday with a decision.").

If second and third round interviews are conducted at a facility, the field of applicants is narrowed based on findings from the first interview. Candidates making it through the first cut are contacted to interview again. These additional interviews are conducted much as the first, but the questions require more in depth answers. Actual task performances are often included during these interviews. Many organizations have different panels of interviewers to conduct subsequent interviews.

Assess the Candidates

Once all the candidates have been interviewed, the final selection process begins. A scoring matrix (Table 6.1) may prove useful to eliminate subjective conclusions and provide an even field for all candidates. Such a system also provides documentation, should a candidate question the final decision. The matrix should be completed based on information gathered during the interview and should be specific, informative, precise, concise, and legible. Each candidate should be rated on his or her responses. Prior knowledge should not be considered in rating the responses of the candidate.

If a panel of interviewers participated in the interviews, each should complete a grid and be given the opportunity to voice observations of the candidates. The panel should be allowed to express concerns or support for individual candidates and to state their reasoning. When a team conducts the interviews, there must be clear guidelines for building a consensus. Will the choice be the candidate with the highest score for the greatest number of interviewers? Will some interviewers' judgments weigh more? Is there a system in place to break a tie? In case of a tie, will the top candidates be reassessed? Who will have the authority to make the final decision?

When faced with equally qualified candidates from which to select, the candidate's personality may become the deciding factor. It is important to choose a candidate that will be able to work with existing employees. A part of the job of manager is observing the behavior of employees. A manager may need to rely on instincts to make a choice from equally qualified candidates.

Table 6.1 Sample Interview Matrix

	High 3	Medium 2	Low 1
1	N/A		
2	Advancement	Close to home	Need a change
3	Education and experience	Education or experience	No education or experience
4	Interpersonal skills/good team player Strong patient care background Adaptability	Average skills and abilities	No special skills or abilities
5	Learning new protocol, workflow, and personnel	Getting to know way around	Unsure
6	Over 10 yrs experience long term employment	5–10 yrs experience 2–5 yrs experience/long term employment	Under 2 yrs experience
7	Good prior experience in same type environment	Some experience in type of environment	No experience in field
8	Assumed responsibility for self and others	Some responsibilities related to field	No responsibilities
9	Achieved several goals/advancements	Some accomplishments	No accomplishments
10	Self-starter Gets along well with others Great skills Adaptable	Dependable Gets the job done Good skills	Undependable Troublemaker Poor skills
11	High interest	Advancement	N/A
12	Education Cross training Research mentor	Education	N/A
13	MA/BS or equivalent	AA or equivalent	Certificate or less
14	College or certificate program	Limited training	No training
15	Certified or registered	Not certified/registered but has equivalent training	Not qualified
16	Looked upon as a leader Good communicative skills	A team player	Does not get along well
17	Describe problem/crisis		
18	Handled appropriately with little guidance	Handled appropriately with guidance	Inappropriate response
19	Able to give information without offending others	Able to give information	Unable to avoid offending others
20	Able to show respect with empathy	Able to show respect	Unable to show respect without offense
21	Learned a new language or jargon Able to show respect without offense	Able to communicate effectively	Unable to adapt style
22	Strong leadership skills Able to allow someone else to lead	Leader Team player	Unable to function as a team member

(Continued)

Table 6.1 Sample Interview Matrix (Continued)

	High 3	Medium 2	Low 1
23	Open		
24	Open		
25	Open		
26	Open		
27	Open		
28	Open		
29	To assist the radiologist and physicians in the diagnosis and treatment of their patients To provide the best patient care To assist the department leadership in any way necessary	To do my job as a member of the team To provide good patient care	To do my job
30	Work environment Opportunity to advance New challenges Home town atmosphere	Work environment Opportunity to grow Locality	Locality
31	Leadership Teacher Team player Work ethics Skills	Team player Work ethics Skills	Skills
32	Does the task with skill and adaptability Pays attention to details	Performs the task with skill and needs little or no guidance	Performs the task with limited ability Needs assistance
33	Same		
34	Same		
35	Same		
36	Same		
37	Able to fulfill all requirements and duties	Able to fulfill majority of requirements and duties	Unable to meet or perform several essential requirements
38	List tasks unable to perform and reasons:		
39	Open		

Totals:

1–5 _____ x 5 = _____   6–12 _____ x 2 = _____

13–15 _____ x 1 = _____   16–23 _____ x 3 = _____

24–28 _____ x 1 = _____   29–31 _____ x 3 = _____

32–36 _____ x 5 = _____   37–39 _____ x 3 = _____

Grand total: _____

Source: Weemploy.com. Interviewing techniques. Available at: http://www.weemploy.com/interviewing.htm. Accessed September 20, 2004.

Checking References

Once the field of applicants has been narrowed through the interview process, work references provided by the remaining candidates should be verified, usually by the human resource staff. References must be checked systematically in accordance with strict guidelines, and no reference checks should be performed in the absence of an applicant's signed authorization. Many applicants prefer their current employer not be contacted. Because of potential legal issues, many employers will provide only minimal information verifying job title, dates of employment, and hiring status.

It is important to document that an organization has made a good faith effort to check references of all potential employees. "Should you be in a position to use personal contacts such as your colleagues in other organizations to check on potential employees, in no way should you ever actively use information so obtained in justifying a decision not to hire a particular person. All reference information used in making employment decisions should be objective (always fact based, never opinion based) and verifiable in the records of the organization providing the information."[2]

When checking nonemployer references, it is appropriate to ask different types of questions. These references are resources for information surrounding the candidate's personality and attitudes. Questions that can be asked include, "Did [candidate] have a problem getting along with others?" "Is [candidate] dependable?" "What type of setting do you think best suits this person?" "Would you recommend [candidate] for this position?" Appropriate nonemployer references are persons who know the candidate professionally, such as their coworkers.

Employment Eligibility

Immigration reform has given employers a new set of legal risks and pitfalls that cannot be avoided. The Department of Homeland Security (DHS) requires employers to obtain proof of identity and employment eligibility. The DHS Form I-9 lists acceptable documents for proof of identity and employment eligibility. Questions surrounding citizenship should always be handled by the human resource staff, when available, not by the hiring manager. If human resource expertise is unavailable, the manager should consult the organization's legal counsel.

Making the Job Offer

Once a candidate is selected, a job offer is extended and salary negotiation begins. Most organizations have established pay scales commensurate with skills and experience (see Chapter 7). The scales may need to be adjusted when the need is critical and the available pool of qualified candidates is limited. During periods of shortages, qualified candidates may have other offers available, and it may be necessary to meet or exceed the other offers in order to sign the best candidate. Once a salary is agreed on, a start date is established and a verbal agreement is made. Many organizations issue a follow up letter confirming the verbal agreement, which is kept on file for further reference.

Follow Up

Appropriate follow up takes very little time, but it is a courtesy due the applicant that serves to protect the image of the institution as an employer in the community. For the selected candidate, follow up consists of making the offer. However, even candidates who do not receive a job offer should receive some form of follow up to complete the interview cycle. A telephone call to the finalists within the timeframe given at the end of the interview takes only a few minutes. All candidates should receive a letter thanking them for their interest and informing them of the decision to extend a job offer to a different applicant. If a candidate is qualified for other positions within the organization, the letter can suggest he or she apply for those positions.

Conclusion

Selecting the right person to fill a vacancy is challenging, but with the right tools and adequate preparation, this process becomes easier. Assessment tools such as interviews and scoring grids are just that, tools. As such, they are not a substitute for managerial judgments but simply an aid to help make the right selection.

References

1. Grieshaber W. The pre-employment interview. *Radiol Manage.* American Healthcare Radiology Administrators. 2005;27(4):14–24.

2. McConnell C. *The Effective Health Care Supervisor,* 5th ed. Sudbury, MA: Jones and Bartlett Publishers; 2003.

Bibliography

Equal Employment Opportunity Commission. Uniform employee selection guidelines questions and answers. Available at: http://uniformguidelines.com/uniguideprint.html. Accessed November 2, 2006

Fogleman S, Anderson D, McCorkle D. Human resource management: employee attraction and selection guide. Texas Agricultural Extension Service. Available at: http://www.temep.tamu.edu/cg/factsheets/rm8-3.html. Accessed September 20, 2004.

Wysocki A. Hiring selection. University of Florida IFAS Extension. Available at: http://www.edis.ifas.ufl.edu. Accessed September 20, 2004

Chapter 7

Determine and Manage Compensation

Steve Gaines

This chapter discusses employee compensation within the context of the imaging facility. Compensation encompasses more than purely monetary considerations to include benefits and intangible rewards. To prevent morale problems and a poor working environment, compensation must achieve 3 levels of equity as perceived by employees: internal, external, and individual. A well designed, consistent compensation plan is the primary mechanism by which pay equity is achieved. The plan provides guidelines to follow when quoting salaries to recruited candidates and in calculating rewards for performance.

Why do people work? Is it to earn compensation to provide for the needs and desires of themselves and their family? Is it for the simple enjoyment of socializing with people they might never have otherwise known? Is it for self fulfillment and satisfaction? People work for these and other reasons, which are not always clear, even to the individual worker. Although money may be a major reason most people work, it is not usually the sole reason they leave a job. Career advancement, skill development, the need to feel better appreciated, or the opportunity to have greater impact on a facility leads people to seek new employment. An effective compensation plan, then, will encompass much more than purely financial considerations and will support employees' less tangible motivators.

Total compensation involves much more than an employee's wage or salary and includes the full range of benefits and "perks" designed to reward an individual's expertise and services performed. A well thought out compensation plan will attract quality applicants, retain employees, and keep morale high, contributing to good patient care.

Psychology of Compensation

In designing a compensation plan, the human resource staff and the imaging administrator need to be aware of the emotional and psychological factors that color perceptions about compensation. Anyone developing compensation plans, for example, must always remember that the compensation is for a job, not an individual. A particular job has a specific value (usually a range) to the organization; no matter how well the employee performing that job does, the amount of compensation cannot rise above a predetermined amount without incurring excessive labor costs and pay inequity. In other words, no matter how dedicated and talented an imaging technologist is, he or she will very rarely be compensated as a radiologist.

This concept of compensating the job, not the person, is a fundamental element in achieving pay equity. According to Robert Solomon, PhD, "Equity is a judgment made by the employee regarding the fairness of compensation."[1] This judgment is comparative, not absolute, and is often unconscious. It is nevertheless crucial to employee satisfaction.

In evaluating equity, employees consider not only the wage and benefit package, but also less tangible benefits such as collegial atmosphere, job status, and working conditions. Employees calculate the ratio of reward to performance for themselves and for others who work either in the same facility or in another organization the employees consider comparable. They compare the ratios. If the 2 ratios are equal, as perceived by the employees, equity is achieved. If an employee's ratio is less than another's, the employee will feel undercompensated.

Some factors influencing the employees' perception of pay equity are beyond an employer's control. Employees, for example, may overestimate their own performance value; they may use inaccurate or incomplete data to calculate the comparison ratio; they may overestimate or underestimate the value of some of the less tangible rewards; and they may compare their situation with a poorly matched individual.

However, the likelihood that employees will perceive pay inequality can be reduced. Should a certain radiologist be allowed to berate and abuse clerical staff? This and other activities that produce a hostile or unpleasant working environment may lead employees to increase the value of the performance half of the ratio ("My performance is worth more because of the environment I put up with."). Well conducted performance evaluations (see Chapter 11) can also impact pay equity perceptions. Here the administrator can honestly and accurately make employees aware of their performance, which improves the quality of the performance half of the equity ratio. A technologist who is informed of unsatisfactory performance is less likely to perceive inequality when he or she receives a below average pay raise.

Importantly, a compensation plan that is equitable when compared both internally among coworkers and externally among local, regional, and national markets can be designed. Constructing such a plan and communicating its value are the focus of the following sections.

Basics of a Compensation Plan

Healthcare, as a whole, has hundreds of positions that require highly technical skills, from positions in the pharmacy and laboratory to positions in nursing and certainly radiology. To keep the salary ranges of these positions in a manageable format, a compensation plan must be put in place. The basic components of the plan should contain a method to differentiate between the required knowledge and skills from one position to the next, should be prepared to adjust with market changes, should be comparable to or exceed others in the industry for a competitive edge, and should consider employee needs and preferences.

Characteristics of a Compensation Plan

Although specific compensation plans will differ among facilities, all share common goals. Employers should seek to reward employee performance and knowledge, maintain internal equity within the organization to retain employees, and maintain competitiveness in the external labor market to recruit new employees. The mission and goals of the organization can be reflected in the compensation plan as well. For instance, if an organization's primary mission is to be a leader in providing compassionate diagnostic care, then the compensation plan must be structured so the organization will be able to attract and retain the type of staff necessary to carry out the mission.

Market changes are inevitable. The compensation plan should have inherent flexibility to allow for sudden changes in the marketplace, healthcare trends, and the possibility of organization and objective redirections by the institution. In other words, changes in the salary market and the facility's goals can occur with little or no notice. The compensation plan needs to be able to address these changes quickly to ensure recruitment of qualified candidates.

Components of a Compensation Plan

Although money (ie, wages and salary) is the form of compensation most employees think of first, it is by no means the only one. A compensation plan should also specify benefits, such as insurances, retirement plans, and time off. A third form of compensation is less tangible, as previously noted. These intangible rewards include safe, pleasant working environment; respectful relationships; and employee recognition activities (see Chapter 14), among others. The intangible rewards may be difficult to quantify, but should at least be noted in communication about employee compensation (see Sidebar 7.1).

SIDEBAR 7.1: Raise Awareness of Total Compensation

One way to help employees recognize the true value of their compensation is to issue a compensation summary at the end of each year. These statements list not only the employee's gross pay total, but also the itemized value of all benefits, including insurance premiums per employee; the cost of sick leave, vacation, holidays, and other paid time off; and the employer contribution to 401k or other retirement plans. See example below.

JOHN DEER
PO BOX 100
LEWISTOWN, PA 17044

February 08, 2005

Dear JOHN:

Below is a summary of selected benefits paid for you by your employer.* This is presented to give you an idea of the value of your employment with the Foundation based on your wages and benefits.

Annualized Wages		**$38,864**
Health Coverage	**$11,337**	
Medical, Prescription, Dental Vision		
Retirement Plans	**$2,074**	
Pension and FHA 401K contribution		
Income Replacement/ Life Insurances	**$1,005**	
Life Accidental Death Dismemberment Ins.		
Long Term Disability		
Workers' Compensation		
Unemployment Compensation		
Employer Paid Taxes	**$2,973**	
Social Security		
Medicare		
Total Benefit Costs		**$17,389**
Total Wages and Benefits		**$56,253**
Value of Benefit Time included in your wages	**$2,990**	
Paid-Time-off (PTO)		
Vacation, Holidays, Personal Days		

Total Benefits Including Benefit Time		**$20,378**	**36.2%**
Wages Paid for Time Worked		**$35,874**	**63.8%**
	Totals	**$56,252**	**100.0%**

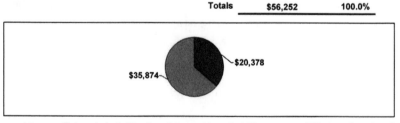

We appreciate your efforts on behalf of the Foundation and hope that this summary will illustrate the value of your employment with us.

Sincerely,

A. Gordon McAleer
President/CEO

* Additional information is available on reverse side.

Source: Sue Reinke, Barbara Eldredge, and Robert Kauffman of Lewistown Hospital, Lewistown, PA.

Wage and Salary

The most common model of monetary compensation for imaging facilities and other healthcare facilities is a standard base pay program. Fixed salary ranges are assigned to each job category, with minimum and maximum annualized earnings. Then, generally, a merit pay program is put into place that offers employees the opportunity to increase base pay each year based on individual performance, helping maintain perceptions of individual pay equity. If the salary ranges are set up equitably and merit raises given based on performance appraisals, the system is also most likely to maintain internal equity, that is, employees will feel they are being paid fairly compared to their coworkers.

In regions where demand for technologists or other categories of workers is highly competitive, the base pay system may be augmented by bonuses and other one time payments, known as variable pay systems. Signing bonuses, in particular, are one time payments to reward new employees for choosing one imaging facility over another. Signing bonuses are often paid in installments (eg, one half after 6 months of employment, one half at the end of a year) to encourage retention. Spot bonuses are rewards given in recognition of an employee's effort, usually immediately after a project or other special performance activity. A third type of one time compensation is the lump sum merit award, often used as a way to recognize ongoing high quality performance by an employee who has reached the top of the salary range. These awards are given annually after the performance review and are not automatically awarded in subsequent years. A retention bonus is also used most commonly when an organization or department is being dissolved and keeping people to a certain date is important.

Healthcare is joining other industries in using various forms of pay-for-performance to reward employees. These plans were once reserved for upper management, and although that is still the case in many instances, newer plans are involving a wider range of employees. They receive a base pay but can earn substantially more if their performance or that of their unit (or the facility) meets or exceeds predetermined goals. The rewards may be in the form of higher raises, larger employer matches of 401(k) contributions, or annual bonuses. However, as Karl Matuszewski, MS, PharmD, has noted, "The goals must be meaningful and clearly understood, not vulnerable to negative unplanned consequences."[2] In other words, if a goal to increase revenues by substantially increasing the number of procedures performed within a specified time frame results in an increase in errors or a decline in patient satisfaction, the pay-for-performance plan has failed.

If bonuses and monetary awards are part of a facility's compensation plan or a pay-for-performance system is implemented, eligibility criteria and performance goals must be clearly spelled out and communicated to all employees to avoid perception of favoritism and a negative impact on internal pay equity.

Laws Governing Wages and Salary

A compensation plan must comply with all federal, state, and local laws. The Fair Labor Standards Act (FLSA) and the 2004 FairPay Regulation that updated the FLSA designate employees who are paid by the hour as nonexempt and those paid on a salaried basis as exempt. Both types of employees are paid at a predetermined base rate, as outlined in the facility's compensation plan and the employment agreement. The FLSA and the 2004 update specify the minimum wage that nonexempt employees are eligible to receive and conditions under which they can earn overtime pay. Overtime pay at a rate of not less than 1.5 times the base pay rate must be paid for each hour above 40 hours an employee works in a work week. The FairPay Regulations revised the categories of exempt (ie, exempt from overtime pay) employees, which include individuals earning at least $455 per week and who meet criteria for job categories such as executive, administrative, professional, and computer professional. In general, exempt employees have control over other employees, can exercise independent judgment in substantial work-related matters, and/or have advanced training or specialized creative skills. The FLSA also defines standards for payroll record keeping and child labor.

In addition, state laws cover a range of issues related to wages and pay. Some states (eg, Connecticut) specify a minimum wage higher than that specified by federal regulations. Other states (eg, California) have overtime regulations that exceed those of the FLSA. Before constructing a compensation plan, information should be collected on all relevant laws and regulations to ensure compliance (Box 7.1).

Box 7.1 Resources for Wage and Hour Laws

Federal

Department of Labor: www.dol.gov
FairPay Regulation: www.dol.gov/esa/regs/compliance/whd/fairpay/main.htm
Internal Revenue Service: www.irs.gov
US Small Business Administration: www.sba.gov

State and Local

Chamber of Commerce
State or city departments of labor, taxation, or small business administration

---

Constructing Pay Ranges

The basis of an effective compensation plan is the salary scale, which sets pay ranges (or spreads) for each job category. Ideally, a multilevel approach will be used that builds both internal and external equity, as follows.

Establish Job Descriptions

These are the basis for all calculations and should include level of supervision, key tasks, responsibilities, and education and special skills required (see Chapter 3). The manager will need to be knowledgeable about the details of each description to carry out further steps in the process.

Collect External Wage Data

A variety of resources are available, with varying levels of precision and accuracy. AHRA compiles and publishes a compensation and benefits survey, with data aggregated by geographic region, organization type, and volume of procedure. Other sources include the US Department of Labor, which compiles data from the Occupational Employment Statistics survey for selected job titles. Data run about 12 months behind collection and are amalgams of data from all regions. Job descriptions are not provided, so it may be difficult to determine comparable responsibilities. The 2007 report, based on mid-2006 data, gave the mean hourly wage for a nuclear medicine technologist as $30.29 (annual $63,000) and for an imaging technologist as $23.71 (annual $49,320).[3] The US Bureau of Labor also publishes the *Area Wage and Salary Survey* that lists earnings for about 80 geographic areas.

Another source of external wage data is salary surveys at nongovernmental Internet sites. These surveys may be sponsored by human resource consultants, recruiters, or nonprofit organizations, and access is often free. Validity may be an issue, especially with surveys that rely on voluntary reporting by readers. However, it may be possible to gather data with geographic precision. For example, the salary wizard on Monster.com (www.monster.salary.com) provides the base pay by job title and zip code, including a median, 25th percentile, and 75th percentile amount.

Commissioned salary surveys are probably the most accurate and specific, but can also be expensive. A consultant can be hired to conduct the survey, which ensures exclusive access to the results but forces the facility to bear the entire cost. Alternatively, healthcare facilities within a state or smaller geographic region can commission a survey, with each participating organization sharing the cost and receiving the survey results (which are anonymous and amalgamated for confidentiality).

Less formal methods may be useful when a limited number of pay ranges are being established. With a few telephone calls, the manager may find colleagues in similar facilities who are willing to share compensation data. Local employment advertisements may also provide wage offerings, especially for nonspecialized job classifications such as receptionist.

Whatever the source, external wage data need to be taken into consideration as pay ranges are being set. Paying competitive salaries is one component of attracting and retaining qualified employees.

Carry Out an Internal Job Evaluation

The process of job evaluation helps ensure internal equity by establishing comparable values for each job description to which compensation figures can eventually be assigned. Although many job evaluation systems exist, 3 of the most commonly used are slotting (also known as classification), ranking, and point factor (or point evaluation).

Slotting calls for establishing the value of a job by comparing and classifying it with other similar jobs. The first step is to identify the various categories of jobs (eg, clerical, direct patient care) and draft a description for each category. Next, the key characteristics of the jobs in each category must be described; these characteristics become the category standards. Finally, each job description must be reviewed and each job assigned to a category based on similarity of tasks performed, the level of decision making exercised, and the job's contribution to the imaging facility's goals.

This system is commonly used by large organizations with multiple locations and job descriptions. Once the categories are established, the system is simple to apply and easily accommodates new jobs. However, the system relies heavily on the subjective judgment of the job evaluator, especially for jobs that could fall within 2 categories.

Ranking is one of the simplest methods and is well suited to smaller facilities with a limited number of job descriptions. The first step is for the human resource department or the imaging administrator to become very familiar with all of the facility's job descriptions. Then he or she ranks each by identifying the job that is the most important to the organization and the one least important. Generally, the valuations are based on levels of independent judgment exercised, responsibility, supervision, and advanced education. Once the highest and lowest ranks have been determined, the human resource department or the administrator examines the remaining positions and identifies the highest and lowest valued, a process that is repeated until all jobs have been ranked.

Although this system is simple, it is subjective, calling for the ability to make a value judgment about comparable characteristics. For example, are the college degrees required for the business manager and imagaing technology manager equivalent? What characteristic distinguishes these positions and makes one of greater value than another? The more complex the jobs, the greater the difficulty in ranking them.

The *point evaluation* method involves, as the name suggests, assigning points to specific compensable factors. The point total equals the relative worth of each job to the facility. This process requires that the human resource department or the imaging administrator identify the compensable factors that the jobs possess and are relevant to the facility. These may include years of experience, knowledge and skill requirement (includes education), decision making authority, and complexity of tasks. Using a point chart, the evaluator compares each job on each factor and assigns a number of points. As shown in Table 7.1, a receptionist job that required a high school diploma and 2 years' experience would gain 110 points for the knowledge factor. The total of all factors represents the job's value relative to others at the facility. Point charts are available commercially (eg, the Hay Job Evaluation System or the Mercer CED Job Evaluation System) or can be constructed.

This method is often considered less biased than the others, but care must be taken not to allow bias to influence the assignment of points.

Establish Benchmark Jobs

In all likelihood, the human resource department or the imaging administrator will be able to find accurate external wage data for only some of the facility's jobs. These become the benchmark jobs from which all pay ranges will be extrapolated.

Match Wages and Salaries to Results of the Job Evaluation

This process will vary depending on the job evaluation method used. If slotting was used, a benchmark job needs to be identified for each category; that job's pay range

Table 7.1 A Point Chart to Value Knowledge Required

Schooling Completed	Years of Experience					
	1	2	3	4	5	≥6
High school diploma	100	110	125	140	160	195
High school + specialized courses	125	135	150	165	185	220
High school + 1 yr college equivalent	150	160	175	190	210	245
Courses equivalent to 2–3 yrs college	250	260	275	290	310	345
Bachelor's degree	310	320	335	350	370	405
Master's degree (or equivalent)	370	380	395	410	430	465
Master's + certification	430	440	455	470	500	535
Doctorate	495	505	520	535	565	600

becomes the range for all jobs in the category. For ranked jobs, wage data for the benchmark jobs are assigned according to the jobs' rankings, then the remaining jobs are assigned higher or lower pay based on their rank. For example, suppose external wage data indicate that medical office managers earn an average of $65,000 and medical receptionists about $28,000. On the facility's ranking, the office manager is ranked 3 (with 1 being the most valued) and the receptionist a 6. Jobs ranked 4 and 5 would be assigned wage values between $28,000 and $65,000.

Finally, if a point system is used, the first step in establishing pay ranges is to assign points to each benchmark job. Then on a simple line graph, plot each benchmark job's points (x axis) and average or median pay (y axis) and connect each plot point. The line makes it straightforward to locate the points assigned to any job needing a pay figure and to find the corresponding amount (Figure 7.1).

Develop Pay Ranges

Also known as spreads, pay ranges provide the maximum and minimum amounts to be paid for each job description. Having spreads is a valuable tool in maintaining internal equity while being able to reward performance or experience. Raises are calculated so employee pay stays within the spread. However, if inflation becomes a problem, a percentage can be applied to all spreads to keep them competitive and equitable; every few years, spreads may need to be reassessed with regard to external equity and adjusted as well.

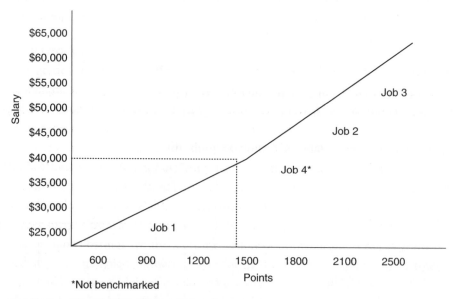

Figure 7.1 Line chart based on benchmark jobs 1, 2, and 3.

Table 7.2 Sample Spreads

Job Title	Salary Midpoint	Range	
		%	Amont
Imaging technology manager	$33,000	±15	$28,000–37,950
Imaging technologist III	28,000	±10	25,200–30,800
Imaging technologist I	23,000	±10	20,700–25,300

There are no hard and fast rules governing the size of a spread. Commonly, spreads at the lower end of the pay scale tend to be smaller (eg, 10% to 20% above and below midpoint) than spreads at the higher end (eg, 20% to 40%) (Table 7.2). Spreads need to be large enough to accommodate raises sufficient to be motivating and to avoid employees reaching the maximum too quickly, thus losing the opportunity for merit raises.

Benefits

Benefits account for about 30% of a facility's payroll costs and are an important factor in achieving external equity and maintaining competitiveness.[4] Although most people are reluctant to discuss their pay details with someone else, they willingly share information about health coverage, vacation time, or tuition reimbursement from their employers. All this information becomes part of employees' pay equity ratio.

In deciding which benefits to offer and at what level, the human resource department or the imaging administrator should consider both external and internal factors. In most markets, competition for healthcare workers is intense. A facility's benefits package must meet or exceed those of its competitors if it is to attract the best workers (Figure 7.2). Some benefits are taken for granted by employees (eg, certain paid holidays), and no competitive advantage is gained by offering them (although not offering them confers a notable disadvantage). However, benefits that are less consistently offered (eg, dental coverage) may contribute to an applicant's decision to join the facility or an employee's decision not to look elsewhere.

Internally, the facility should aim to offer benefits employees value. These will vary based on factors such as the employees' age, marital status, length of service, and level of education. A workforce that is predominantly aged 25 years or younger, single, and new to the facility is less likely to value a generous retirement plan than a flexible work schedule. A facility that seeks to attract and hold more mature workers may consider offering professional development and a matched 401k retirement plan. A survey of employee benefit preferences, using a 1 to 5 scale, for example, might be a low cost way to involve workers in these potentially costly decisions.

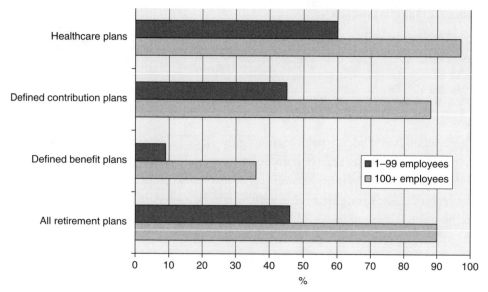

Figure 7.2 Percentage of private businesses offering retirement and healthcare benefits (March 2006).

Source: US Bureau of Labor Statistics, Department of Labor. National compensation survey: employee benefits in private industry in the United States, March 2006. Available at: http://www.bls.gov/ncs/ebs/sp/ebsm0004.pdf. Accessed June 22, 2007.

Another way to give employees a say in benefits is to offer a cafeteria plan. In one type, the full flexible benefits plan, each employee is given a "benefits budget"; after the cost of certain facility wide benefits (eg, paid vacations, basic health insurance coverage) is deducted, the employee chooses the benefits he or she wants. These plans have the additional advantage of letting employees know the actual costs of benefits as part of their total compensation.

Employment benefits in the United States fall within 2 broad categories. Mandatory benefits involve the employer, employee, and government, which mandates participation. Social Security, Medicare, and Worker's Compensation fall within this category (Box 7.2).

Voluntary benefits encompass all other non-monetary benefits an employer can choose to offer. These can be categorized into 4 areas: insurances, time, retirement, and quality of life.

Box 7.2 Resources for Mandated Benefits and Taxes

US Treasury: www.irs.ustreas.gov
State tax sites: www.taxsites.com/state.html
US Small Business Administration: www.sba.gov

Insurances

Although primarily a human resource department function, an imaging administrator should be knowledgeable of the process behind selecting providers of health insurance, as well as life and disability, for a group of employees. In some parts of the United States, health purchasing alliances have been created to provide access to group policies to alliance members, which are usually small facilities that are not large enough to negotiate good premium rates. The local medical society is one source for information on an available alliance.

In many instances, however, the best solution is to work with an insurance broker, who may represent 10 to 15 different insurers. The broker will be able to not only streamline the comparison process, but also provide information on the financial stability and claims payment history of the insurers. He or she can suggest cost saving measures and options not previously considered. The broker may also be aware of the level of coverage being offered by similar facilities in the immediate geographic region. Box 7.3 provides tips for finding and selecting a broker.

Before meeting with a broker, however, a basic understanding of the types of coverage available, as well as the needs of both the employees and the facility, should be understood.

Box 7.3 Finding an Insurance Broker

Sources include:

- Colleagues in other imaging or healthcare facilities
- Yellow Pages
- State insurance department (all brokers must be licensed by the states they operate in)
- National Association of Health Underwriters: www.nahu.org
- National Association of Insurance and Financial Advisors: www.naifa.org

Before a broker is selected, the following questions should be considered:

- Does the broker represent several insurers offering the type(s) of insurance needed (ie, disability, life, medical, dental, vision)?
- Does the broker sell insurance full time, rather than as a sideline?
- Do the broker's clients include businesses that are similar in size and insurance coverage needs to that of the imaging facility?
- Is the broker a member of one or more relevant professional associations?
- Does the broker have one or more of the following professional certifications?
    - CLU: Chartered Life Underwriter
    - RHU: Registered Health Underwriter
    - LUTCF: Life Underwriter Training Council Fellow
    - FLMI: Fellow Life Management Institute Program

Health Insurances

Health insurances include medical, prescription drug, dental, and vision plans. According to the US Department of Labor, 71% of workers in private industry had access to health insurance, and most must pay at least a portion of the premiums.[5] Although increases in the cost of medical premiums have slowed, providing this form of insurance equals about 8% of payroll.[4]

Of the 3 types of medical insurance, the traditional fee-for-service plans offer the greatest flexibility to those covered but carry the highest premiums. Basic coverage includes services in the physician's office, some tests, and some hospital costs. Major Medical covers what Basic coverage does not, in general, as the name suggests, the major expenses associated with surgery and hospital care. A Comprehensive plan would include both Basic and Major Medical coverage.

Under a traditional plan, employees can choose any physician they want and seek care in any hospital. Each year the employee has to pay a deductible before the insurance begins to pay, usually covering 80% of the cost, with the employee paying the remaining 20%. If the provider charges more than the insurance plan's "customary fee," the employee must pay the entire excess amount.

The second type of medical insurance is the health maintenance organization (HMO). Essentially, these plans require that covered employees use a physician and other providers who are either employed by or contracted with the HMO. Employees pay a small copayment for office visits and certain other services, but the HMO pays the remaining amount. Little or no paperwork is needed after the patient's first visit. Full coverage is provided for physical examinations, childhood immunizations, and other preventive care. In most HMOs, the patient's primary care physician must provide a referral to any necessary specialists in order for the HMO to pay for these services.

The third type of medical plan, the preferred provider organization (PPO), incorporates the positive features of both HMOs and traditional plans. Employees must still use a physician and other providers within the plan's network to have the lowest copayment and the least paperwork. However, employees can seek care out-of-network; the cost will be partially paid by the plan with submission of claim forms. Generally, preventive care is fully covered, and only a small copayment is needed for other in-network care.

Outpatient prescription drug plans offer employees the ability to purchase many prescription drugs at substantially reduced rates. Drugs must be on the plan's formulary and the prescriptions must be filled by network pharmacies, which include most of the major chains.

Dental insurance is also available in traditional, HMO, and PPO plans. Generally, although the primary characteristics are like those of the medical plans, dental plans have annual capitation on the amount of services covered and involve copayments and/or deductibles. Most plans cover preventive services such as regular cleanings, but may only cover 50% of more expensive specialized services such as crowns.

Dental discount plans are not insurance. There are no premiums and patients do not receive reimbursement for out-of-pocket expenses. Instead, these plans have negotiated with participating dentists to provide services to member patients at deep discounts over the American Dental Association pricing code. Patients do not have to seek preapproval for major procedures or lose coverage because of preexisting conditions.

Vision plans are generally simple and basic, covering up to 1 eye examination and a pair of glasses per year. Some also cover at least a portion of the cost of contact lenses or LASIX corrective surgery. Vision providers often contract with a medical plan, so coverage is provided in a single package. In such cases, the vision plan follows the same general guidelines as the medical plan (ie, if added to an HMO, the vision plan would follow the HMO procedures and guidelines for seeking care, copayments, etc). Noninsurance vision discount plans are also available.

In selecting any type of health insurance for an organization, the following should be looked at carefully:

- Amount and timing of deductibles
- Amount of copayments (should be less than 25% of the fee for the service)
- Range of services offered and relevance to workforce (a facility with a preponderance of female employees will want good obstetrics-gynecology coverage)
- Level of coverage for preexisting conditions and long term illnesses
- Level of annual and/or lifetime maximum coverage

Life Insurance

Life insurance is available to about half of all workers in private industry, according to US Department of Labor statistics.[5] Nearly all employers who offer life insurance pay the full premium for their employees, and many offer employees the option of purchasing life insurance coverage at the group rates for family members. Employees do not have to take a physical examination, and coverage is provided even for employees with preexisting conditions. Most plans allow employees to convert the policy to an individual one, if they change employment. Level of coverage is either a prespecified flat dollar amount or a multiple of the employee's annual salary.

Disability Insurance

Disability insurance is available as short term or long term coverage. Short term disability plans pay at a rate of about 60% of the employee's gross weekly pay for up to 26 weeks when an employee is unable to work because of off-the-job injury, illness, or pregnancy. Several states (eg, New Jersey and California) require that employers provide short term disability coverage through a state operated program.

Long term coverage usually picks up where short term coverage ends, with a waiting period between 30 and 180 days. Most plans pay up to 60% of the employee's gross income until he or she reaches the age when Social Security coverage begins.

Employers are often more willing to provide short term coverage than a long term plan because they want the employee to recover and return to work. Organizations that are considering disability coverage benefits should review the plans in terms of the following:

- Length of the exclusion period (before benefits begin)
- Limitations related to preexisting conditions
- Range of disabilities covered
- How and by whom disability is determined
- Level of and by what means payments will be made

Time

With a finite number of hours in a day and many workers seeking a balance between work and family, paid time off (PTO) can be one of the most valued benefits any employer can provide. Of course, it carries a cost—up to 10% of payroll by some estimates is spent on PTO.[6] In addition, for an imaging facility, patients must still be served, insurance claims must still be filed, and bills must still be paid, so work schedules may need to be adjusted each time an employee is absent from his or her job.

PTO may include some or all of the following:

- **Vacation:** The number of vacation days often increases with seniority, with new employees receiving about 10 days, those with 5 years' seniority receiving 15 days, and anyone working 10 or 15 years earning 20 days. Days are accrued on a monthly or quarterly basis. One issue that must be considered is whether unused days can be carried over to the following year. Vacations are a valuable way to reduce stress, prevent burnout, and maintain health. Allowing carry over may encourage those employees most in need of time off to forego the opportunity. A carry over policy also can create record keeping hassles for payroll staff. However, the policy provides some flexibility for workers who would otherwise lose the benefit and could lessen the likelihood of the "year end rush" to take remaining vacation days.

- **Holidays:** For most organizations, holidays are days when the facility is closed, unless it provides emergency imaging services. Thus, the financial and patient impact is potentially greater than for vacation or other forms of PTO. Although 9 to 11 paid holidays are standard, the facility's patient flow may affect the selection of holidays, which will vary somewhat from year to year. For example, if Christmas falls on a Tuesday, designating Christmas Eve as a holiday may make sense, as few patients will seek appointments. Facilities that serve a predominantly non-Christian community may want to follow the community's major holiday schedule.

- **Sick leave:** Like vacation time, sick leave contributes to an employee's health and well being. Furthermore, it can lessen the likelihood of illness spreading to other employees or to patients, who may have weakened immune systems. Six to 9 days are average, and many employers allow employees to use sick days to care for a sick child or other relative. Allowing sick days to carry over is less common than with vacation time; as a result, employers often experience a higher level of absenteeism in December as employees use up their sick days. Some facilities encourage employee wellness by "buying back" a portion of sick days from employees with a perfect attendance record. This may, of course, have the unintended consequence of discouraging employees to take sick days when truly needed.

- **Personal time:** Although not as universal as vacation time, personal time off is a benefit used by some employers to accommodate life's unforeseen events. One type, used in conjunction with vacation and sick leave, offers 2 or 3 days annually that an employee can use as needed (with supervisor approval)—bereavement, chaperoning a child's school trip, or moving into a new home, for example. A second version, used by about 25% of private employers, puts vacation, sick, and personal days off into a single pool of 15 to 17 days.[6] The employee can use the time for any purpose (eg, a long vacation, an extended illness, or volunteering to build a Habitat for Humanity home). As with vacation time, the number of days increases with seniority. Accounting for time off is simplified because employees no longer have 2 or 3 categories of hours that time off must be assigned to, but simply 1 large pool to which all time off is assigned.

- **Jury duty:** Although federal labor laws do not require employers to provide PTO for jury duty, some state laws do (eg, Connecticut). Two weeks is the average benefit, with the employee going onto unpaid leave for the duration of jury service (during which he or she receives a modest stipend from the state). Before establishing a jury duty benefit, the human resource department should verify any regulations through the state department of labor or the jury administration office of the department of justice.

In planning the benefits package, 2 additional forms of unpaid leave, both mandated by the federal government, should be reviewed:

- **Family/medical leave:** The Family and Medical Leave Act (FMLA) of 1993 specifies that employers with at least 50 employees working within a 75 mile radius must allow eligible employees to take up to 12 weeks of unpaid leave a year, either as consecutive weeks or in smaller intervals. See Chapter 1 for more information on FMLA.
- **Military leave:** Individuals serving in the active military and the reserves have a number of protections related to civilian employment, outlined in the Uniformed Services Employment and Reemployment Rights Act of 1994. In general, service members who are on active duty for up to 5 years are guaranteed reemployment at the level they would have achieved had they not left for military service. The employer must provide training if necessary to enable the returning employee to assume the new position. The employee's benefits, seniority, and pay are to be as they would have been without military service, and all non-seniority rights remain as if the employee had simply taken a leave of absence. If the employee has been on active service for less than 31 days, he or she remains eligible for the employer's health benefits; if serving 31 days to 2 years, the employee may be asked to pay the full premium to continue health coverage.

Flexible scheduling

One other "time" benefit is flexible scheduling, or flex time, which is based on the premise that the workday/week does not have to be 9 AM to 5 PM, 5 days per week. In fact, because imaging facilities are likely to be open more than 8 hours a day and on Saturdays to best serve their patients, flex time can be one way to keep expanded hours without hiring additional workers.

Flexible scheduling can involve employees either working 4, 10 hour days or adjusting their arrival and departure times over a 5 day work week, the latter probably being more appropriate for an imaging facility. If a receptionist begins work at 7 AM and leaves at 4 PM and the second begins at 9 AM and ends at 6 PM, the front desk is covered for 11 hours. If the facility's workforce is large enough to have all key positions filled and enough employees can and will flex their time, the facility has gained 3 hours of time to serve patients with the same staff as before flex time.

If employees are involved in setting up the schedule using a template to achieve appropriate levels of coverage, there is less likelihood that issues of unfairness will arise. It is probably also a good idea to apply the new schedule for a trial period and analyze the results before making permanent changes.

Retirement Plans

A defined benefit pension plan is usually employer funded and pays the retired employee a predetermined, specified sum based on number of years of service and final salary. These plans are disappearing, however, and are rarely available in smaller organizations because the plans are expensive, highly regulated, difficult to administer, and not portable when employees change jobs. Therefore, this section focuses on defined-contribution plans, specifically the 401(k) plan.

The 401(k) has been available since 1978 and is offered by about 90% of larger businesses and about 45% of smaller ones. These plans allow employees to contribute up to a specified limit in pretax dollars automatically deducted from their pay. Their employer may match their contribution, again to a limit. Additional after tax employee contributions are allowed as well. The limits are set by the federal government and the employer and change each year. All contributions are invested under the direction of the employees, who receive frequent statements. These enable the employees to track the progress of their retirement savings and increase their contributions if they want.

In addition to tax advantages and the potential for growth throughout investment, 401(k) plans offer employees and employers several other advantages. Unlike defined-benefit plans, 401(k) plans can move with an employee to another employer. Savings can continue to grow; even the employer matched funds remain with the plan if the employee has worked a specified number of years (usually 4) to become vested, which is motivation to remain at the facility. The plans are relatively easy to set up and administer; mutual fund and other investment companies actually do the work and even assist with meeting all regulations. These plans are also less costly than defined-benefit plans; the facility's matching contribution (which is optional but recommended for competitiveness) can be adjusted each year in light of the organization's performance.

Quality of Life Benefits

Finally, a compensation plan can include a variety of benefits that contribute to employees' professional and personal quality of life, including:

- **Professional development:** These programs can include tuition reimbursement, conference attendance, dues for memberships in relevant professional organizations, office subscriptions to professional publications, and in office "lunch and learn" workshops and guest speakers. Such activities encourage employees to enhance their skills and show respect for them as professionals. Guest speakers can be offered at no cost, whereas other activities may have a cost to consider, such as tuition reimbursement. In setting up a professional development program, a budget, based on estimated costs, the size of staff, and a maximum amount needs to be established. Talking with colleagues may be useful in arriving at a reasonable figure. Criteria and policies for applying for funds must be clearly spelled out and cover all professional employees, to avoid issues of inequity.

- **Employee Assistance Program (EAP):** Family stresses, drug abuse, mental health problems, and a death of a loved one are just a few of the non–work-related issues that can affect an employee's work performance. EAPs are independent, confidential referral services that will assist employees in obtaining mental health and other social services. For an annual fee based on projected usage, the facility contracts with the EAP. The employee pays no fee for the referral service, although he or she is responsible for any fees from the ultimate service provider (if not covered by insurance). Employees can seek assistance without the employer's knowledge or, in the case of an employee with a performance issue, can be referred to the EAP. These programs may be available through local social service agencies, hospitals, or United Way agencies.

- **Wellness programs:** Many local hospitals, medical centers, physicians, and for-profit wellness providers will contract with the imaging facility to offer wellness activities either at the workplace or the provider's facilities. These can include healthy eating demonstrations; health fairs; and talks by experts on stress reduction, exercise, and weight reduction. Larger facilities may want to sponsor a Weight Watchers group for employees. Many of these activities can be provided at little or no cost to the facility. Employees may have suggestions of offerings and could be responsible for administering these activities.

- **Discounts:** Not all benefits have to cost money or involve administrative time. For example, many businesses are eager to offer discounts to employees. These range from local fitness centers to national theme parks. An employee committee could be set up to identify the types of activities employees would be most interested in, locate reputable businesses and determine their offerings, and prepare a plan for employee access.

Conclusion

An imaging facility's employees spend a significant portion of their daily lives serving patients and others to ensure the operation's success. They deserve fair and equitable compensation for their efforts. A compensation plan that takes into consideration a wide array of financial and non-monetary compensation is fundamental to ensuring that equity.

References

1. Solomon RJ. *Clinical Practice Management.* Gaithersburg, MD: Aspen Publishers; 1991; 88.

2. Matuszewski KA. The new pay-for-performance plans. *Pharm Ther* 2003;28:758.

3. Bureau of Labor Statistics. National employment and wage data from the Occupational Employment Statistics survey by occupation, May 2006. Available at: http://www.bls.gov/news.release/ocwage.t01.htm. Accessed June 25, 2007.

4. Auxillium West. Compensation and benefits. Available at: http://www.auxillium. com/pay.shtml. Accessed June 22, 2007.

5. U.S. Bureau of Labor Statistics, Department of Labor. National compensation survey: employee benefits in private industry in the United States, March 2006. Available at: http://www.bls.gov/ncs/ebs/sp/ebsm0004.pdf. Accessed June 22, 2007.

6. Obringer LA. How employee compensation works. Available at: http://money.howstuffworks.com/benefits.htm. Accessed June 22, 2007.

Chapter 8

The End of the Employment Cycle

Roberta M. Edge

Employees will leave, either involuntarily through layoff or dismissal, or voluntarily. And when conflict is a part of the process leading up to the end of the employment cycle, an important skill for imaging administrators and other managers is the ability to manage it. Interpersonal conflict is a source of employee dissatisfaction and low morale and can negatively affect patient care. Administrators can choose to avoid a conflict, force a resolution, seek accommodation, reach a compromise, or seek a productive collaboration. In all cases of an employee leaving an organziation, though, procedures should be in place to handle the change consistently and legally. The end of the employment cycle can provide valuable information to improve the work environment to benefit the remaining employees.

For a variety of reasons, both voluntary and involuntary, employees leave jobs, even in the best managed organizations. Life changing circumstances such as the birth of a child or relocating for a spouse's new job, the lack of career advancement opportunities with the current employer, layoffs, or poor job performance are just a few circumstances that will set the last part of the cycle of employment in motion.

An involuntary termination is initiated by the employer, for 1 of 3 reasons: just cause (ie, the employee violated a policy or exhibited a behavior such that termination was justified); a reduction in force (also called an RIF, downsizing, or a layoff), which may result from budgetary cuts, a reorganization, or a merger; or poor job performance. In the case of layoffs, advance notice is generally provided, along with outplacement or other counseling services. Employees initiate voluntary terminations and ideally provide at least 2 weeks' notice in writing of their intention to leave the organization.

Imaging administrators who experience a rise in the number of terminations unrelated to layoffs should take steps to identify the causes and make changes where appropriate. Chapter 14 discusses the use of employee satisfaction surveys, and later in this chapter, exit interviews are highlighted as a source of valuable retention information.

Developing a working environment that has minimal interpersonal conflict can also contribute to high retention rates.

Conflict Resolution

During the course of any given day in an imaging facility, conflicts can arise between employees: a radiologist and an employee, a patient and an employee, or a group of employees and the organization (Box 8.1). The imaging administrator is often called on to help resolve these conflicts and needs to understand the dynamics of conflict, its possible causes in the workplace, and various tactics to achieve resolutions that reflect organizational policy.

Conflict is generally the result of 2 different perspectives on a topic whether between 2 individuals or between people and an organization. It is inevitable in a complex setting in which people are passionate about their work. Some organizations view conflict as a negative thing and choose to ignore it, hoping it will go away (it probably won't). Others view conflict as a signal for the need to analyze processes and policies to create a better environment for the good of the team. Successful organizations seek to achieve resolution because unresolved conflict can cause morale and productivity problems, even among employees uninvolved in the actual conflict, and can have negative consequences for patient care.

Causes of Workplace Conflict

Personal differences, an informational deficiency, role incompatibility, and environmental stress are the 4 most common causes of conflict in the workplace. Conflicts involving personal differences are the most difficult to resolve, "as they can become highly emotional and take on moral overtones."[1] The individuals become fixated on who is "right"; as long as they are attached to a moral position, they are quite unwilling to let go of their view. Informational deficiency, more popularly referred to as "failure to communicate," is probably the most common cause of conflict. This less

---

Box 8.1 Tips to Avoid Conflict

Although conflicts are inevitable, managers can take steps to reduce them, including:

- Communicating often and honestly with staff
- Providing mechanisms for staff feedback and responding quickly and appropriately
- Encouraging employee problem solving and team building skills
- Keeping everyone focused on providing the best care for patients and working in the patients' best interests

---

emotionally charged type of conflict responds well to management techniques described below and can often be avoided altogether with the communication techniques outlined in Chapter 14.

Conflict over role incompatibility erupts when the goals of one department are not aligned with another. For example, when a physician orders a series of "stat" tests on a hospitalized patient, conflict may arise among the responding staff. Who has the priority in the patient's care: the imaging technologist who is there to obtain portable images, the phlebotomist to draw blood, the respiratory therapist to give a breathing treatment, or the nurse to administer pain medication? Front line staff are left to sort it out, usually based on "who got there first."

Environmental stress such as organizational financial woes, immediate work area functionality, uncertainty over work schedules, or rapid and constant change can fuel the flames of conflict. This type of conflict is often intense and directed at trivial issues. Feeling that their surroundings are out of control, employees seek to regain a sense of control by focusing on issues over which they feel they still retain control.[1]

Techniques To Deal With Conflict

As a conflict becomes apparent, the manager has several options for dealing with it immediately: avoid it, force a resolution, seek accommodation, reach a compromise, or seek a productive collaboration. The first 2 can be ineffective in that by forcing a resolution or avoiding it altogether, the administrator prevents the involved parties from having an investment in the long term resolution of the conflict and runs the risk of being viewed as dictatorial, weak, or ineffective. No one is served by letting the conflict continue to fester instead of doing the work to bring it to resolution; over the long term, the simmering conflict can prove detrimental to the functioning of the workgroup.

Seeking accommodation pushes for maintaining a friendly atmosphere but does not address each person's rights or provide a full evaluation of the source of the conflict. Yet accommodation can be effective in some circumstances. For example, when a policy is the source of the conflict, employees can be coached to follow the policy until it can be discussed and perhaps changed at a higher level of management.

Compromise is effective as long as it is not overused or does not become the only strategy a manager uses. Compromise means everyone involved in the conflict will "give to get" and is best used when there is no simple solution to the source of the conflict.

Collaboration is the one solution that focuses everyone's attention on the problem and fosters a "you and I against the problem" view rather than each party remaining vested in "us against them" thinking. Collaboration challenges the participants to think of the best possible solution for the patient. Perhaps the most important thing a manager can do once a collaborative resolution is reached is to guide those involved to "forgive and forget," so the resolution can take hold and both parties can move on with their work.

When 2 employees disagree over specific work issues, the administrator may only need to encourage them to resolve the issue within a specific timeframe, rather than personally intervene for a resolution. Just the fact that the manager is aware of the conflict and will intervene if a resolution is not found may stimulate the employees to end the conflict. If it continues beyond the deadline without progress toward resolution or the conflict involves several parties or more fundamental issues, the administrator can intervene with a 10 step protocol[2]:

1. Draw all parties' attention to the facility's mission, values, and goals, which may be the basis for a resolution.
2. Put the facts on the table, asking each party to clearly and concisely describe the conflict, who is involved, and what the effect has been.
3. Enlist the cooperation of all involved parties to reach a resolution.
4. Remain impartial and, if necessary, identify others who can serve as mediators.
5. Actively listen to all parties, asking questions, taking notes, and summarizing what has been said to ensure accuracy.
6. Find areas of commonality between both sides that can be the basis for a resolution.
7. Have realistic expectations for the outcome, accepting that complete agreement may not be possible.
8. Accept that compromise may be the best outcome and does not represent failure.
9. Set a realistic time frame for resolution to encourage all parties to work on the issues; if progress is being made when the deadline is reached, be flexible about extending it, but impose a resolution or seek mediation if stalemate occurs.
10. Follow up periodically after resolution to ensure all parties remain committed to the agreement.

Consultants as Peacemakers
Healthcare employees' job satisfaction depends on their feeling valued, having a certain amount of control over the work environment, providing good patient care, having a structure for career advancement, being supported with adequate

staffing, perceiving good organization of day-to-day activities, and having equipment and supplies available. If several employees become dissatisfied and create ongoing conflict and morale problems within the facility or department or if conflicts seem to occur more frequently or with greater intensity, it might be useful to bring in a consultant to help refocus energy in a more positive manner. Professional mediators can intervene in a specific dispute that the imaging administrator has been unable to settle, but employees may benefit equally well from training on communication, conflict management, negotiation techniques, and team building. This training can be provided by computer courses (eg, the Mediation Training Institute at www.mediationworks.com) or through in house workshops presented by independent consultants or members of the facility's human resource department.

In the case of widespread conflict arising from dissatisfaction, one approach is to develop a consultant led employee group that will learn conflict management techniques, along with working toward diffusing dissatisfaction. All employees should be invited to participate, but their participation can be optional, with financial incentives for those who do so. Preferably, the group should include both clerical and technical staff and equal numbers of those who are satisfied with their work environment and those who are not. Guided by the consultant, the group assesses the current environment, compares it to the department history to clarify the current reality, and then works together to create a vision for the future. Group members are encouraged to disseminate what they learn at each session throughout the department, so other employees see the outcome as coming from their peers and not from management. Information is shared by copying handout information, describing what was learned over breaks and meal periods, and inviting feedback from employees outside the core group. Once established, the group continues to meet on a monthly basis to reinforce lessons learned with their coworkers to keep the conflict at bay.[3]

Terminating an Employee

It will be necessary to terminate employees on occasion. The employee's poor job performance may fail to respond to coaching or retraining. Employees may be found to have committed a work-related crime or failed to follow major policies. Conflict can erupt into violence. Whatever the reason, termination may be the only course of action, but it must be carried out carefully and in accordance with all relevant laws. Human resource staff and/or the facility's attorney should be consulted as soon as termination is an option and remain involved throughout the process.

Rules of Termination

In a report prepared for the Society of Human Resource Management, labor attorney Francis T. Coleman assembled 10 Cardinal Rules of Termination[4]:

1. Never summarily discharge.
2. Get all the facts to make sure the investigation is thorough, complete, and well documented.
3. Conduct all employee interviews with care and deliberation.
4. Investigate promptly—don't delay.
5. Always use the final filter approach (discussed later in the chapter).
6. Pinpoint the basis of discharge.
7. Whenever possible, inform the employee in person.
8. Always use progressive discipline and keep appropriate documentation.
9. When done with the investigation, take action.
10. Beware the set up.

Employees should never be discharged on the spot, regardless of how serious the situation seems, as this puts the employer at risk for a wrongful termination lawsuit. A better solution is to place the employee on leave, paid or unpaid, pending investigation of the incident. If the investigation shows that discharge is warranted, then all documentation and the employee's final paycheck can be gathered for the final meeting with the employee. If the allegations turn out to be false, the employee can return to work. No pay will have been lost: in the case of paid leave, wages continued during the investigation; for an unpaid leave, the employee receives all back wages at the investigation's conclusion.

Investigating an Incident

Involuntary terminations must be conducted promptly, thoroughly, fairly, and consistently. Unless layoffs are involved, terminations usually begin with an incident that requires investigation. Allegations of policy violation, blatantly unacceptable behavior, and/or poor job performance must all be properly and discreetly investigated and appropriately documented in a written report. Before starting the investigation, the imaging administrator should consult with the human resource staff, upper management, or the facility's attorney to ensure that the proposed approach is valid and that the appropriate questions will be asked. It is important to avoid having to return to interviewees for further clarification once the initial meeting is held (M. Mortensson, personal communication, 2006).

Investigations require an objective, dispassionate investigator to follow the facility's policy and stay within federal and state laws while conducting the investigation.

The investigator may be the employee's direct supervisor, the imaging administrator or director of imaging, or a human resource representative. The investigator must be open to evidence from both the employer's and employee's perspective because there may be a reasonable explanation for the employee's behavior. It is critical that the investigator remain open minded until all evidence is gathered.

Investigations must be thorough, and documentation is key. It should include the who, what, where, when, why, and how of the occurrence and, especially in a safety incident, offer possible suggestions to prevent repetition of the incident. As with all human resource issues, the manager should be consistent in the information collected and documented. The investigator should interview the employee and any witnesses to the alleged offense and gather any records that may provide clarity, including the specific policy that was violated, if relevant. All investigations need to be prompt (within 48 to 72 hours of the event or notification of the event) whenever possible, and the employee should be informed of the results of the investigation within 24 hours after the investigation is completed.[4]

Investigation seeks to pinpoint exactly what the employee did that violated policy or warrants dismissal. This is not the time to dredge up other infractions that are not pertinent to the investigation; rather, the goal must be to obtain all information relevant to this case and document it fully. If it is determined that the employee is to be dismissed, a proven, substantiated reason or reasons for the discharge should be cited in writing. The employee will receive a written copy of the reason for termination. If the employee appeals the termination, files for unemployment benefits, and/or brings a lawsuit, the reason for discharge is legally discoverable and the employer must be able to defend its action.[4]

A person who did not directly investigate the incident should conduct a final filter review of the report. This objective person, usually a human resource staff member or the facility's attorney, will determine if everything is complete, look for bias, review recommendations, and check to be sure that the recommendation for discipline or discharge in this case follows precedents set in the organization for other similar incidents. The final filterer will also determine if legal counsel is needed in this particular case.

Termination Meeting

Once a decision has been made to dismiss an employee, he or she should be told promptly. If the employee has threatened a staff member, has a history of violence, or is psychologically impaired, the facility's attorney should handle the termination, in conformance with state labor laws.

In most cases, however, the termination meeting can take place face-to-face and will usually include 2 management level staff members, including the imaging administrator, a human resource representative, and/or the employee's immediate supervisor. Among the suggestions for conducting an effective meeting are[5]:

- When possible, hold the meeting early in the week, so the employee can immediately begin the job search, and at the end of a workday, so the employee will not have to face coworkers or patients while upset.
- Hold the meeting in a quiet, private setting and give instructions not to be interrupted.
- Start the meeting by clearly telling the employee he or she is being dismissed and briefly explain why. Give the employee a written copy of the reason(s) for termination.
- Review any previous discussions or disciplinary actions that were taken *related to the reason for discharge*. Keep any discussion of the employee's shortcomings brief and to the point.
- Listen carefully to any complaints the employee makes. Like an exit interview for a voluntary termination, this is an opportunity to identify issues that could affect other employees' performance or job satisfaction. At a later time, carefully consider whether changes need to be made, based on the employee's comments.
- Explain the employee's rights and benefits, which may include a severance package, access to COBRA (Consolidated Omnibus Budget Reconciliation Act) health coverage, and unemployment benefits. Give the employee copies of the severance agreement and literature from the state employment development or labor department.
- Be prepared to answer questions about 401(k) or pension plans and give the employee contact information for following up on these benefits.
- Ask the employee to turn over keys, identification badge or building access card, the facility's credit card, laptop computer, and any other facility property.
- Give the employee a check covering outstanding compensation, accrued vacation and/or sick leave, severance pay (if any), and any expense reimbursement due. Some states (eg, California) require payment of all wages at termination, but even if it is not legally required, doing so ties up one more loose end and may help the employee feel less vulnerable.
- Arrange a mutually beneficial time for the employee to collect personal items at the facility.
- Try to end the meeting on a positive note but do not promise a good recommendation or help in finding another job.

Occasionally, a manager will encounter employees who know "all the loopholes" and may be using an incident or policy to "set up" the employer for a lawsuit. Some of the signs that employees are preparing to sue include demanding any comments about performance be put in writing, wanting copies of their personnel file, drawing attention to their protected status (eg, age, disability, sex, or race), requesting copies of and/or engaging in discussions about policies related to termination, inquiring how other employees have been treated in similar situations, and/or asking how benefits are paid out at termination. (In many states, the employee has a right to employment documentation, so the manager should check with human resource staff or the facility's attorney if the question arises.) If decisions about the employee's performance have been supported by facts and are appropriate, the documentation may dissuade the employee's attorney from taking the case (M. Mortensson, personal communication, 2006). Managers who treat all employees equitably and fairly and who abide by facility policy are likely to avoid an employee being able to say "the company was out to get me."[4]

A Summary of Laws Relevant to End of Employment

Older Workers Benefit Protection Act

Before 1967, some corporations engaged in practices that removed workers aged 40 years or older from their jobs as a cost saving measure through a reduction in force, or layoff. These layoffs often included a severance package that involved early retirement, a practice that had a disproportionate impact on older workers. In 1967 the US Congress passed the Age Discrimination in Employment Act (ADEA) to prevent employers from discriminating against employees on the basis of age at any point in the employment cycle. In 1990, the ADEA was amended with the Older Workers Benefit Protection Act to require employers who want to use early retirement to reduce their workforce to obtain a waiver that allows the worker to relinquish the ADEA rights, provided the waiver is signed knowingly and voluntarily. Specifically, the act defined *knowingly and voluntarily* as part of an agreement between employer and employee that is written in plain English and that fulfills the following[6]:

1. It specifically references ADEA rights and claims.
2. It does not waive rights or claims that may arise after the agreement is signed.
3. It is executed in exchange for additional consideration (anything of value) to which the employee is not already entitled.
4. It advises the employee to consult with an attorney before signing.
5. If the agreement is between an employer and a single employee, the employee is given 21 days to consider it.
6. If the waiver is for a group of employees, then 45 days are given for the individuals to consider it, and it must contain information about the group

affected, eligibility criteria, time limits, ages, job titles, and organizational units included and those who are not.

7. Once the waiver is signed, the employee must have at least 7 days to revoke it.

At-Will Doctrine

In the United States, employees of most private businesses work under the doctrine known as employment-at-will. Either the employee or the employer can terminate the employment relationship for any reason and without notice, unless otherwise bound by a written contract that specifically states the employee be terminated for cause. For facilities governed by a collective bargaining agreement, the employer must show just cause and have a grievance procedure in place.[7]

There are 3 exceptions to the employment-at-will doctrine: (a) the public policy exception, (b) implied contract exception, and (c) covenant of good faith and fair dealing exception. Currently, only 6 states—Alaska, California, Idaho, Nevada, Utah, and Wyoming—recognize all 3 exceptions; and 4 states—Florida, Georgia, Louisiana, and Rhode Island—do not recognize any of them.

Under the public policy exception, an employee is considered wrongfully terminated if the termination violates an explicit, well established public policy, such as firing an employee for filing a worker's compensation case or for refusing to break the law on behalf of the employer. The public policy could be from a state's constitution, statutes, or administrative policy. Most states, except Alabama, Florida, Georgia, Louisiana, Maine, Nebraska, New York, and Rhode Island, accept the public policy exception. This exception was necessary to create a "proper balance between the employer's interest in operating a business efficiently and profitably, the employee's interest in earning a livelihood, and society's interest in seeing its public policies carried out."[7]

The implied contract exception covers situations in which the employer makes an oral or written representation to employees about job security or any procedures that will be followed in the event of an adverse employment action (eg, layoffs). Employee handbooks are the most common source of an implied contract: any language that says employment will continue as long as the employee does his or her job implies the employer must have just cause to terminate an employee. A manager's comment during a performance evaluation that the employee has a long future with the facility is another example of an implied contract that could eventually lead to a wrongful dismissal lawsuit if the employee is subsequently terminated. The implied contract exception is recognized in 38 states (Box 8.2).

Box 8.2 States Recognizing the Implied Contract Exception to the Employment-at-Will Doctrine, as of October 2000

Alabama
Alaska
Arizona
Arkansas
California
Colorado
Connecticut
District of Columbia
Hawaii
Idaho
Illinois
Iowa
Kansas
Kentucky
Maine
Maryland
Michigan
Minnesota
Mississippi
Nebraska
Nevada
New Hampshire
New Jersey
New Mexico
New York
North Dakota
Ohio
Oklahoma
Oregon
South Carolina
South Dakota
Tennessee
Utah
Vermont
Washington
West Virginia
Wisconsin
Wyoming

This list is provided as general information and is not a substitute for legal or other professional advice.

Source: Muhl CJ. The employment-at-will doctrine: three major exceptions. *Monthly Labor Rev* 2001;124:3–11.

The covenant of good faith exception is recognized by only 11 states (Box 8.3). It paints the broadest brushstroke in defining the employment relationship as a covenant of good faith and fair dealing between every employee and employer. As a result, in the states that recognize this exception, any termination must have just cause.

Exit Interview

Although the need for a termination meeting is clear for employees who are being dismissed, the value of an exit interview for employees voluntarily leaving may seem less clear cut. Nevertheless, human resource experts fully support asking all such employees to take part in an exit interview. There are 2 reasons for conducting these interviews: to improve the organization and to provide closure for the departing employee to ensure he or she feels good about the time spent working at the facility. If the imaging facility does not have a formal policy covering these interviews, the imaging administrator and/or human resource staff should develop one. There should also be a mechanism for analyzing and reporting the results.

Less agreement exists, however, on other aspects of exit interviewing, including the timing, who does the interview, and the format. The traditional time for conducting an exit interview has been the employee's last day, but this is often an emotion filled day occupied with last minute transitional activities and peer celebration. The interview will probably be less stressful and more productive if it is held either several days before or after the final day. If it occurs after the employee leaves, he or she should be asked for the best time to call within the next 7 to 10 days and told that the interview is an important component of the facility's efforts to improve the workplace.[8] Conducting the interview by telephone after departure means the cues from body language will be missed, but the telephone conversation may also encourage the employee to be more honest than in a face-to-face meeting. Waiting a few days also gives the employee time to collect his or her thoughts.

The person conducting the interview must be a skilled listener, able to express empathy, and trained to gently probe for useful details. He or she must also be able to remain calm and unaffected if the employee uses the interview as an opportunity to vent pent-up emotions and frustration. The interviewer should not be the employee's direct supervisor. Among the options, depending on the size of the facility, are a human resource representative, a manager of a unit other than that within which the employee worked, the employee's mentor, or an independent consultant.

Using a standard set of questions will give the exit interview structure and allow for comparison of the findings from one employee to another (Box 8.4). Some organizations give the employee a written questionnaire, which may or may not be followed by a face-to-face or telephone interview. Others use the questions to guide an informal conversation during which the interviewer takes careful notes of the employee's responses.

Box 8.4 Sample Exit Interview Questions

When you interviewed for the job at this facility, was the job presented to you accurately?
Why did you accept the job at this facility?
Were your expectations met?
Why have you decided to leave?
What did you value about working at this facility?
What did you dislike about working at this facility? What would you change about your job?
Did you share your dissatisfaction with anyone? If so, what happened?
What could your supervisor do to improve his or her management style or skill?
Did you receive adequate feedback about your day-to-day performance?
Did you clearly understand and feel a part of the effort to achieve the facility's mission?
Did you have the tools and supplies you needed to carry out your job? If not, what was missing?
What would you suggest to help us create a better workplace?
What aspects of your new job led you to accept it?
What are the qualities and skills we should seek in your replacement?
Would you recommend the facility as a good place to work for your family and friends?
Would you consider working for the facility in the future? If not, would any changes make you do so?

Source: Heathfield SM. Perform exit interviews: exit interview questions. Available at: http://humanresources. about.com/od/whenemploymentends/a/exit_interview.htm. Accessed January 26, 2008.

> **SIDEBAR 8.1:   Reminders for Dealing with a Termination**
>
> 1. Whether a voluntary or involuntary termination, conduct an exit interview.
> 2. Resolve involuntary terminations promptly, thoroughly, fairly, and consistently.
> 3. Investigations require objectivity and a dispassionate investigator.
> 4. Document thoroughly and have everything reviewed by a human resources specialist or an attorney.
> 5. Progressive organizations view conflict as a time to review processes and policies to create a better environment.
> 6. Informational deficiency is the most common cause of conflict.
> 7. Follow the rules of termination.
> 8 Know the labor laws that govern your state.

Once the interview results are available, analyze them in conjunction with earlier results and evaluate whether action is needed. Although each interview is a unique situation, the results have been shown to be valid. An analysis of exit interview statements from 2 major organizations found that 3 to 6 months after leaving, 90% of the employees cited the same top 3 reasons for leaving as they gave during their exit interview.[9] Among the trends to look for are the following[5]:

- Top 3 reasons employees have left
- Top 3 positions with the most frequent turnover
- Average length of employment
- Patterns of turnover based on unit, manager, or department

The results of exit interviews provide a backward looking view of the facility that can help round out the findings of ongoing employee surveys, focus groups, and other retention tools.

Conclusion

Whether voluntary or involuntary, part of the employment cycle is leaving an organization to go on to other opportunities. Even imaging administrators who work in facilities with a dedicated human resource staff are wise to become well versed in this final phase of the employment cycle. See Sidebar 8.1 for some helpful reminders.

References

1. Lipcamon JD, Mainwaring BA. Conflict resolution in healthcare management. *Radiol Manage* 2004;26:48–51.

2. Weiss GG. How to handle conflict. *Med Econ* 2004;81:58–62.

3. Edge R. The gift of employee dissatisfaction. *Radiol Manage* 2002;24:36–39.

4. Coleman FT. Cardinal rules of termination. Available at: http://www.shrm. org/hrresources/lrpt_published/CMS_000943.asp. Accessed August 8, 2006.

5. Brown J. Conducting exit interviews: how organizations can benefit. UN Online Network in Public Administration and Finance. Available at: http://unpan1.un.org/intradoc/groups/public/documents/UN/UNPAN02 1834.pdf. Accessed January 26, 2008.

6. Tola FA, Ramsey CK. What is an employer to do? Employment termination, severance and waivers. Available at: www.shrm.org/hrresources/whitepapers_ published/CMS_000245.asp. Accessed November 1, 2002.

7. Muhl CJ. The employment-at-will doctrine: three major exceptions. Monthly Labor Rev 2001;124:3–11.

8. Barada PW. Before you go . . . conducting exit interviews. HR Magazine 1998;43:99–103.

9. Frase-Blunt M. Making exit interviews work: properly collected and analyzed data can provide valuable insight into employees' attitudes. HR Magazine 2004;49:109–114.

3 Training and Development

Chapter 9

Employee Orientation and Training

Deb Lopez

Effective employee orientation and training programs are not just nice gestures; they are criti-cal to improved customer service, higher productivity, and improved employee satisfaction. Managers should not be satisfied with just basic programs, but should strive for effective and excellent ones. With the ongoing labor shortage in the healthcare field, developing complete and effective employee orientation and training programs is essential. A quality orientation program should educate the employee to the history, values, and goals of the organization and department, as well as provide the new employee with the tools to navigate through the new system. A quality training program that encompasses on-the-job, informal, and formal sessions will help attract and retain high performing employees and improve services.

One of the most important principles to convey during a new employee orienta-tion and any stage of training is the organization's commitment to continuous learning and improvement. This commitment benefits both the organization and the individual employee. Offering ongoing training and continuing education opportunities can aid in recruitment and retention and shows employees that they are valued. A learning environment encourages employees to ask questions, solve problems, and make decisions for themselves.[1] Employees whose skills are kept up-to-date and who know what is expected of them are confident and less likely to make mistakes. They may be more willing to apply best practices and better able to adapt to new technology and procedures, giving the facility greater flexibility to respond to changes in the local healthcare market and meet the needs of their patients.

For the purposes of this chapter, training encompasses a wide range of educational activities, ranging from a new employee's orientation to tuition reimbursement for college courses. Imaging departments within major healthcare facilities or large imaging centers may have dedicated human resource staff responsible for some training activities, but every imaging administrator is likely to be called on to over-see on-the-job training and to contribute to designing and implementing orienta-tion and training sessions for their staff.

Orientation: The Basics for New Employees

Employee orientation can be performed in many different ways and is often developed based on the size of an organization. It can be performed by one person or by a variety of experts. It can be done in large or small groups and can be broken up by type of information. The orientation should meet both the emotional and informational needs of a new employee. An orientation to an imaging facility may be broken up into several components from organizational information to specific department and job duty information. In addition, technologists will need specific on-the-job training for the computer systems and imaging equipment that they will be using and information such as examination routines, age-specific information, required documentation and safety concerns specific to individual imaging modalities, specific pieces of equipment, and contrast material delivery.

Arguably, orientation begins during the interview process. As a hiring manager proceeds through the interview, a prospective employee will gain a sense of what is important to the organization and what role he or she may play in the delivery of patient care. A candidate interviewing for a position is also developing perceptions about the organization and employees by observing the environment: is the department organized, does it look like people are enjoying what they do, are employees attentive to their customers/patients, and are proper safety procedures being followed?[2] While walking a prospective employee through the department, the manager should recognize that there is some initial orientation going on. After the tour, any questions the interviewee has regarding his or her observations should be answered and, if a poor practice was observed, it should be addressed, including how a supervisor might normally give that employee feedback about it.

Some organizations use a "Prospective Employee Kit."[2] This kit can be provided during an interview, as well as during recruitment fairs and when presenting employment opportunities to a class of graduating students. This kit can help an applicant decide if a particular organization is a good fit for them. A prospective employee kit might include the following items:

- Name, address, and telephone numbers of the organization and a contact person within the department
- A brief history of the organization with the organizational values, mission, and goals (Box 9.1)
- Pay periods and vacation and time off policies
- Medical and dental plans
- Paid holidays
- Specific job descriptions

Box 9.1 Sample Organizational Values Statement

Santa Clara Valley Medical Center
ORGANIZATIONAL VALUES

The Values Story

In January 1998, at the request of SCVMC Administration, 31 employees representing a cross section of departments and all levels of staff, management, and physicians created the first draft of an organizational values statement. Following this, it was reviewed and revised by an additional 175 employees working in small groups. In October 1998, the Values Statement was approved and accepted as policy by the VMC Executive Team, Santa Clara Valley Health and Hospital Administration, and the Santa Clara County Board of Supervisors. The following, written by our employees, expresses our beliefs and serves as a foundation for our behaviors, decisions, and relationships:

At Santa Clara Valley Medical Center, we conduct ourselves and provide services for the following fundamental values that are at the heart of who we are:

PATIENTS ARE THE PRIORITY

- We provide quality treatment
- We uphold the dignity of our patients and treat them with respect and compassion
- We incorporate the goals of our patients and families into the care we provide

ONE TEAM WORKING TOGETHER

- Management and staff are in partnership to fulfill the goals of the organization
- We demonstrate mutual respect, trust, and support
- Our communication is effective and reflects honesty, sensitivity and integrity
- We hold ourselves, individually and together, accountable for our actions and job performance
- We recognize, value, acknowledge each other's unique contributions and accomplishment, and support each other as equals
- We give constructive feedback and encouragement
- We appreciate our diversity

PROFESSIONAL COMPETENCE AND EXCELLENCE

- We are a well-trained, competent workforce striving to provide excellent services
- We are empowered to continue our personal and professional growth and effectiveness

USER-FRIENDLY PHYSICAL ENVIRONMENT

- We provide safe, clean, inviting, and accessible facilities
- Employees and volunteers have the equipment and supplies needed to support our work

RESPONSIBILITY FOR RESOURCES

- We utilize our resources responsibly and ensure our financial health to effectively fulfill our mission
- We actively seek out and obtain new sources of funding and resource

RESPONSIBILITY TO THE COMMUNITY

- We are a critical resource for the whole community
- We create and maintain a respected reputation and positive image in the community
- We are perceived as a trusted partner and dependable community resource

Source: Santa Clara Valley Medical Center, San Jose, CA

- Salary ranges
- Sign on bonus information, if applicable
- Local area information

After a job offer has been accepted, a warm welcome into the organization will go a long way toward making a new employee confident that he or she has made the right choice. The time between a job offer and an employee's start date is likely a mixture of excited anticipation and anxiety. Therefore, a letter (Box 9.2) combined with information new employees will need or want to know before their start date will help them through this time period. The welcome letter should include confirmation of the start date and time; where, when, and to whom the employee should report on the first day; and who to call for answers to any questions. The letter should also include the organization's dress code and an orientation outline so the new employee will know what information will be received and when. A new technical

---

Box 9.2 Sample Welcome Letter to New Employee

[DATE]

[NAME AND ADDRESS]

Dear [NAME]

Welcome! I am delighted that you have accepted the position of Staff Radiologic Technologist and look forward to welcoming you personally when you come to work on [DATE]. A few things that might be helpful for you to know before your first day begins at 8:00 AM:

There are designated employee parking lots located on both sides of the hospital. Just follow the signage. We are located on the second floor of the hospital. RTs may wear clean scrubs or street clothes and a clean white lab coat.

During your first 30 days, you will receive a department orientation with [NAME], our Chief RT, and other members of the staff. We want you to feel welcome and comfortable as you begin your career at HMC.

We are dedicated to providing excellent diagnostic imaging services to our patients and their physicians, and to do so while providing each patient with an outstanding personal experience while in our care.

I know that it is never easy to make the decision to change jobs, and that your first few days will be a bit stressful as you begin to work with new colleagues and radiologists. We have a first rate department comprised of many good people who will make you feel at home in a very short period of time. Relax and learn; this is going to be a wonderful opportunity for both you and us to get to know each other. I know that having you join our team is going to make us an even better department. I hope that you will be a part of HMC for a long time to come.

If you have any questions, you can reach me at 908-555-1234, and [NAME, CHIEF TECH] at 908-555-0123. Again, thank you for choosing Hunterdon, and welcome!

Sincerely,

[NAME AND TITLE]

Source: Hunterdon Healthcare System, Flemington, NJ

---

employee may also be provided with the department routine sheets. Some employees may want to review them before job specific training.

Most healthcare organizations require a physical examination to make sure a healthcare worker is physically capable of doing the job he or she is hired to do and all immunizations are up-to-date. The welcome letter should provide information about this appointment and how the results will be communicated to the new employee.

In some organizations, a new employee may meet directly with a human resource benefits administrator, either privately or in a group. Some organizations invite the new employee's spouse to attend these informational sessions as well. The benefits administrator will review the various medical, dental, and life insurance plans with new employees so that they understand the options they have and what costs, if any, are the employee's responsibility. A lot of information is typically given in one of these sessions, so the information should also be provided in writing to allow employees to review the material over a period of several days before deciding on the options they will choose.

The human resources meeting may also be the time to complete any miscellaneous forms and employment documents like emergency notification forms and tax withholding information. This may also be a good time to provide the new employees with a parking sticker or parking card and have a picture taken for their employee identification badge.

At the same time the new employee is sent a welcome letter, the current staff should learn of the new hire, as a memorandum and/or at a staff meeting. One way to help introduce a new employee is to have him or her complete a short questionnaire, which can then be posted (Box 9.3). When the new employee arrives on the first day, coworkers will already know a little about him or her, and common interests may be quickly identified. For example, if the new employee lists softball as an interest, a staff member can mention the department team. Any welcome conversation can include comments about a mutual interest or commonality.

If the new employee will be assigned to a desk, the space should be clean and inviting, with all of the tools needed to do the job (eg, chair, computer, telephone, business cards, office supplies).[3] A technologist working in multiple areas of the department will need an assigned locker, as well as a nametag, dosimetry badge(s), and lead markers.

Organization and Department Overview

Orientation may be held formally in a group at a larger facility or more informally in a smaller or one-on-one setting at a smaller facility. The department

orientation may need to take place over a number of days depending on the size and complexity of the organization. Presentations by various leaders in the organization are typically given. These leaders should be able to convey an understanding of the material and have empathy for the anxiety of a new employee.[4] Information should be presented in both written and oral form. Part of the orientation should touch on the department's policy and procedure manual. Once the basics have been covered, the new employee should be assigned to read the entire policy and procedure manual, followed by a session where the material is reviewed and questions are answered. See Sidebar 9.1 for some key items from a policy and procedure manual that should be pointed out to the employee at this time.

SIDEBAR 9.1: Information To Highlight from the Policy and Procedures Manual During Organizational and/or Departmental Orientation

- Parking regulations
- Identification badges (where worn, what to do if lost)
- Overtime and comp time policies
- Time off request procedures
- Health Insurance Portability and Accountability Act (HIPAA) regulations/ confidentiality statement
- Pager procedures
- Telephone use
- Non-smoking policy
- Patient identification procedure
- Quality improvement programs
- Patient ethics
- Patient rights and responsibilities
- Professional attire policy
- Family and Medical Leave Act (FMLA)
- How the work schedule is created and how to read it
- Departmental agreement (if applicable) and involuntary shift assignments
- Required elements of an imaging request (order) and what to do if not present
- Contrast material administration
- Patient/technologist relations
- Department organizational chart
- Occupational Safety and Environmental Compliance
- Orientation to compliance activities
- Emergency preparedness
- Hazardous material overview
- Infection control
- Security management
- Employee bargaining units if the organization is unionized

A good orientation helps ease a new employee's transition into the organization, ignites his or her excitement and enthusiasm, and gets the employee up to speed faster. It provides the perfect opportunity to instill in the employee the values and corporate culture of the organization.[3] Orientation also meets the educational and informational requirements mandated by outside agencies such as the various state health departments and radiologic health branches, Medicare, and The Joint Commission. These outside entities mandate both what needs to be included in orientation/training and what must be documented.

Take a Tour

A good way to start a department-specific orientation is to take the new employee on a tour of the department, making introductions to other employees throughout the tour. The employee should be introduced to key employees, such as the time-keeper, all supervisors, and the radiology chair. Having a bulletin board in the department that displays photographs of all the staff members, along with their name and position, is a great way for new employee to learn who everyone is.[5] Housekeeping staff assigned to the area and the students who are rotating through it should also be introduced.

During the tour, areas such as the employee lounge, bathrooms, and bulletin boards should be pointed out. New employees should also be shown where payroll forms such as overtime slips, time off requests, and shift swap requests are kept and where work schedules are posted. They should be shown where lockers or other designated spaces for personal belongings are located and have appropriate keys assigned to them. In addition, bulletin boards containing important information such as employee notices, dosimetry readings, and information pertaining to the student technologist training program should be identified.

After the department tour, a tour of the entire facility should be conducted, high-lighting the cafeteria, vending machines, cash machine if available, and mailboxes. This tour is just to point out where certain conveniences are; a tour of the operating room and the other areas a technologist might need to know while performing portable work can be done during orientation specific to those assignments.

Safety
The safety portion of the orientation should be given special attention. It is highly recommended, and sometimes required, to document the date this instruction takes place, with a space on the checklist for the employees to initial, indicating they have been given the information, have had the opportunity to ask questions, and understand the information. This document should be kept in the employee's file or wherever the facility requires such documentation to be stored.

Safety items that should be included in the orientation include the facility's required response to the following:

- Code red (fire)
- Cardiac arrest
- Bomb threat
- Security stat
- Infant and child abduction
- Disaster (code triage)
- Security threat

- Armed security threat
- Hazardous material incident
- Radiation protection
- Dosimetry badges, where to wear, how and when to exchange, and how to read report
- Declaring pregnancy for radiation monitoring purposes

In addition, the following information needs to be reviewed, and the employee should be shown where to find this information:

- Universal precautions and the supplies needed to follow these precautions
- Infection control
- Emergency buttons
- Patient occurrence reports
- Supervisor report of employee injury
- Eyewash stations
- Fire extinguishers and alarms
- Emergency exits
- Hazardous materials and material safety data sheets
- Oxygen shut-off valves
- Emergency bathroom key

In an organization that provides clinical training to students, employees who are assigned to work with them should be oriented to the students' curriculum and supervision and how to complete a student evaluation form. It is helpful to provide an example of a form that has been completed in a way that provides meaningful feedback to the student.

The orientation items listed are meant to serve as a guide that can be used to create an orientation checklist. As items from the list are discussed/taught to the new employee, there should be written acknowledgment (eg, an employee's initials) that the subject has been covered. This is helpful when asked by a regulatory or accreditation agency to provide evidence of training, or when an employee's performance is reviewed and if and when they were trained/oriented to a particular procedure or policy needs to be verified.

There is a great deal of information that needs to be presented, so some of the information should be provided in writing. The new employee should also be told how to access this information in the future, whether it be online or in a printed policy and procedure manual.

Training New and Experienced Staff

At its core, training is about change. It can help an employee change the way he or she carries out a task or prepares for forthcoming technological changes. It can change attitudes. It can help an organization adapt to a changing environment through its staff. The most effective training ties closely to an organization's mission statement and strategic plan and grows out of the employees' career development plans (see Chapter 10).

In a small imaging center, the imaging administrator may be responsible for setting up a training program, identifying suitable training methods, and even conducting some of the training. Even in imaging departments within hospitals or other large facilities with dedicated human resource staff responsible for training, the imaging administrator is likely to be involved in needs assessment, content design, and course evaluation. To get the greatest benefit from every training dollar, the imaging administrator needs to understand how adult learning happens and then design training that uses these principles to their best advantage.

Fundamentals of Adult Learning

More than a century ago, educational psychologist Edward Thorndike identified 3 principles that guide how adults learn. Even training with 21st century computer techniques is most effective when it is structured on these laws.

The first principle, *readiness*, recognizes that adults learn best when they are ready to learn. They know and accept the reason to learn, the learning objective is clear, and they have the knowledge or skills needed to understand and use the new information. Thorndike's second principle of adult learning is *effect*. Adults learn best when the effect of learning is positive (ie, positive feedback and the pleasure of successfully mastering a new skill). The principle of *exercise* calls for hands on learning, simulations, repetitive practice, and other techniques that personally involve and engage the learner while giving him or her multiple chances to try out new skills or knowledge.

Effective training incorporates content and methods that build on the fact that adults learn best[6]:

- When they are ready to learn
- What they actually perform
- From their mistakes
- What is familiar to them

- With emphasis on different senses
- Methodically and systematically
- Only what they can understand
- Through practice
- When they can see their progress
- When information is presented in a manner that is unique to them

To put these principles into practice, the imaging administrator should offer training that:

- Has clear objectives that are communicated to participants
- Offers opportunities for active, hands-on learning
- Provides an atmosphere within which failure or errors are allowed, with constructive feedback
- Relates the new information to existing knowledge and skills
- Uses multiple teaching techniques that call for using most of the senses (see Box 9.4)
- Breaks complex material into manageable segments and concentrates on a few key points developed around a simple structure
- Provides enough background so participants can understand why they need to learn the information and how it fits into their work
- Gives opportunities to practice the skill or apply the new information during or immediately after training and in situations that closely resemble those of the workplace
- Provides feedback through tests, constructive criticism, dialogue, and self evaluation
- Takes advantage of participant differences (eg, teaming more experienced participants with less experienced ones in case-study analysis or presenting benefits specific to participant's job)

These principles should underlie every training opportunity. If training is being designed and presented internally or on-the-job by a member of the imaging or human resources staff, the principles can guide program development. When an external training program is being considered, these principles can help evaluate its potential effectiveness.

Structuring the Internal Training Program

In devising a workshop or other training session, the instructor has 4 primary tasks. The first is to develop clear learning objectives that will let everyone know what to expect from the training. The second is to prepare a lesson plan that will

Box 9.4 Putting the Senses to Work

Each person tends to favor one sense over another when it comes to learning. Trainers can take advantage of this individuality by using a wide range of teaching techniques and aids for each training session. Training consultant and author Garry Mitchell has categorized these aids according to the 3 most commonly used senses in the classroom:

Sight
Diagrams
Charts and graphs
Training manuals
Flip charts
Reference materials
Lists of definitions
Sample transactions
Films and videotapes
Slides and PowerPoint presentations
Actual situations to be observed
Demonstrations
Satellite audiovisual conferencing
Interactive CD-ROMs and other computer-based learning
Virtual reality sessions

Sound
Discussions
Demonstrations
Question and answer sessions
Panel discussions
Group projects
Lectures
Films and videotapes
Audiotapes
Satellite audiovisual conferencing
Interactive CD-ROMs and other computer-based learning
Virtual reality sessions

Kinesthesia (hands-on)
Simulations
Paper and pencil tests
Flowcharting
Case histories
Group projects
Role playing
Interactive CD-ROMs and other computer-based learning
Virtual reality sessions
Supervised practice on the job

Source: Mitchell G. *The Trainer's Handbook: the AMA Guide to Effective Training.* 3rd ed. New York, NY: American Management Association; 1998.

organize content and give structure to the presentation. The third is to select which teaching method(s) to use so as to observe the laws of learning and incorporate as many of the principles of learning as possible. Finally, every training session needs to be evaluated for its effectiveness in achieving its objectives and meeting the needs of the staff and organization (discussed at the end of this chapter).

Write Clear Learning Objectives

Probably no step in designing a training session is more important than setting clear objectives. They specify what will be learned and how it will be taught and evaluated. In his book, *The Trainer's Handbook: The AMA Guide to Effective Training*, Garry Mitchell lists 5 criteria for effective learning objectives for skill-based, or cognitive, training[6]:

1. The objective describes an action the trainee will perform.
2. This action is described specifically and in detail.
3. This action is measurable or observable.
4. This action is realistic.
5. The objective usually includes a time frame within which the action will be completed.

The focus is on the trainee, not the trainer; that is, the objective does not describe what the trainer will do, but what the trainee will do once training has been completed. The answer to that question is the objective, for example:

- Participants will perform a full mammogram on the new XYZ scanner within 10 minutes with 0 retakes.
- Participants will pass a final test with a score of 75 or better.
- By the end of the second session, trainees will create a 1 page document that incorporates a 5 column table from supplied data.

Of course, not all training is cognitive; some seek to change attitudes, what is called affective learning. Objectives for affective learning are more abstract than for cognitive learning and may take longer to evaluate. Nevertheless, they can and should be defined as specifically as possible. Mitchell suggests that because most feelings or attitudes result in observable actions, the objectives can relate to those actions. For example, declines in rates of absenteeism and tardiness can reflect changes in morale and motivation. Fewer patient complaints are an indication of an improved attitude toward patients, so the objective might be: *Patient complaints related to reception staff will decline by 75% within 90 days*. Although some attitudinal change can be assessed immediately by pre- and post-tests, in many other cases, evaluating whether an objective has been met may require observation and/or measurement over a period of time, as specified in the objective.

Prepare a Lesson Plan

The lesson plan provides a structure for the training content and helps the trainer ensure that the 10 principles of learning are incorporated into the session(s) by defining not only the content, but also the methods to be used. Its 4 primary parts are:

1. **Introduction:** The first part of the session meets participants' needs to understand, be ready to learn, put the training in context, and become involved. This is accomplished by providing the learning objectives; asking trainees to describe a problem or situation related to the training topic; and leading participants to acknowledge the need for training through questions, discussion, and/or case example.
2. **Information:** Participants' needs to understand, learn in a systematic fashion, use their senses, and feel unique are met during the second part, as the topic's key concepts are explored. The trainer can ask questions that lead participants to discover a concept; the trainer can show a short videotape or give a short lecture that may be followed by a case study or group discussion. Attention spans tend to last only about 20 minutes, so presenting concepts 1 at a time and using a variety of teaching methods are important.
3. **Practice:** Every training session should include some form of practice (eg, simulations, role playing, case studies, or actual hands on exercises). Such activities meet trainees' needs for understanding, using their senses, learning from their mistakes, experiencing success, constructive feedback, expressing their uniqueness, and active learning.
4. **Evaluation:** Before trainees leave the training session, the depth of their understanding and learning should be evaluated to meet the trainees' needs for feedback, understanding, learning from their mistakes, and experiencing success. This may be as simple as a paper and pencil pre- and post-test, or more complex, such as a group presentation of a case study for the other trainees and instructor to evaluate. In some cases, such as skill-based technical training, the evaluation may occur as an integral part of the practice phase. In either instance, the lesson plan should define how evaluation will be carried out and relate to the learning objectives.

Charney and Conway have identified 4 levels of evaluation that should be carried out[7]:

1. Trainees' feedback to the training session
2. Trainees' understanding of the key concepts
3. Trainees' behavior that reflects their learning
4. Quantifiable changes that have resulted

The lesson plan includes details for level 2, but the trainer should also outline how and when the other 3 levels will be evaluated. The overall evaluation process is discussed in further detail at the end of this chapter.

Select the Training Method(s)

As suggested in the previous section, there are many ways to train adults. Except for the simplest of concepts, most training should incorporate more than 1 method to allow for differences in learning styles and provide variety to enhance comprehension and retention. Budget, trainer capabilities, the number of employees to be trained, and the type of content (cognitive or affective) affect the selection of method. The 2 general categories of learning methods are self-directed and trainer-led.

Self-directed learning can be accomplished with manuals, books and magazines, videotape or audiotape presentations, or computer-based technology, including the Internet, CD-ROMs, or the facility's intranet. Most forms are low to moderate in cost, and the trainee is in control of when, where, and how to learn. This is particularly advantageous to facilities with multiple sites, for whom the logistics of gathering all trainees together may be a deterrent. Self-directed learning is useful to teach skills and information that the trainee will use individually, rather than in a group (eg, creating an Excel worksheet or operating the new radiology information system). Interactive CD-ROMs lend themselves to problem-solution learning and to situations in which job skill requirements change frequently.

However, the individual nature of most self-directed learning techniques make them less effective in teaching content that involves relationships (eg, patient relations or team building). Also, if a large number of employees need to learn a topic by a specified date and with a high degree of standardization, self-directed learning may not be the most effective method. Self-directed materials tend to be generic, relying on the learner to put the information into context for his or her job. Finally, self-directed learning has a higher dropout rate than trainer-led learning.[7]

Trainer (or facilitator)-led learning allows the trainer to control much of the learning process and provides opportunities to discuss reactions, lending itself to relation-based content. It is also the format employees are most familiar with because it closely resembles the learning format used in the US education system. The trainer can customize content and use case studies and examples from the trainees' work situations.

Organizing a trainer-led session, however, can involve considerable cost, time, and logistical support. A training consultant can be hired to present a program (see Box 9.5), or the imaging administrator or other staff member can create one. The consultant may involve more direct cost, but the staff member will need time away from his or her job to develop and present the program. In both cases, support will be needed to locate a suitable site, prepare handouts and other materials, and log attendance and evaluations. Attendees will need time away from their job to participate.

The multiple needs of adult learners demand that trainers use a variety of techniques to present their message. Ideally, each session would incorporate several of the following techniques:

- **Lecture:** To be effective, the trainer should talk for no more than about 15 minutes at a time and then use another method to continue the learning process.
- **Written materials and handouts:** These should be used sparingly to convey facts or provide resource material for the trainees to refer to when they are back on-the-job.
- **Audiovisual presentations:** Videotape, audiotape, and slide and PowerPoint presentations are best used in short (10 to 20 minute) segments (eg, to provide a visual demonstration of technique). They should never merely repeat information the trainer gives.
- **Demonstrations:** For optimal learning, these should be kept simple and cover only key steps; subsequent discussion should refer to the demonstration to reinforce learning and ensure that everyone has taken the same crucial message(s) away from the demonstration.
- **Panel discussions:** These are an ideal way to present multiple points of view, engage the group in controversy, or to explore trends.
- **Class discussions:** By asking questions, the trainer can engage the group, assess the level of understanding, and augment content with the trainees' experiences.

Discussion can also be created by breaking the group into smaller groups to discuss a specific topic and report back to the entire group.

- **Role plays and other simulations:** After a presentation of theory or technique, trainees are given the opportunity to demonstrate how they would apply the technique in a setting as close to on-the-job as possible; an observer offers immediate feedback. Role plays can also be used during the introduction by having trainees demonstrate how they currently act; this "before" can be referred to during the session and compared with an "after" role play.
- **Case histories:** After learning 1 or more points of knowledge, trainees are given a case study to read and analyze, usually with the aid of questions provided by the trainer. This tool can be used as a form of practice or to evaluate the trainees' learning.
- **Project sessions:** Assigning a project is an effective tool to tie new knowledge to established knowledge and skills. Ideally, the project is one that can be carried out on-the-job or at least that closely relates to the trainees' work. Most projects will involve applying multiple new skills.
- **Games:** Learning can be fun, and games can be an effective way to introduce a concept, give participants a common experience on which to base future discussion, demonstrate their learning, or increase receptivity to learning. To be effective, however, a game should be followed by a brief discussion to tie the activity to the learning objectives or key points being demonstrated.

Research has shown that learners retain about 10% of what they read, 20% of what they hear, 30% of what they see, 50% of what they see and hear, and 90% of what they say and do.[6] Clearly, to get the most for every training dollar invested, the trainer needs to apply a wide range of methods to help participants retain as much as possible.

Selecting External Training Programs

An alternative to developing an in-house training program is to send employees to external offerings. These may be available at professional conferences, through public seminar organizations, or at educational institutions. When purchasing new equipment, off site training at a vendor's facility is either mandatory or offered as a line item option.

Professional Organizations

The conferences for professional organizations such as the American Society of Radiologic Technologists (ASRT) and AHRA offer a range of panel discussions, continuing education workshops, and speakers that can provide selected staff members with unique opportunities to learn best practices and new skills targeted to their professional needs. Only a limited number of employees can attend at any one time, of course. One way to get greater value for the dollars spent is to require the attending staff person to share key handouts and make presentations to other staff shortly after returning from the conference. Plans to attend a conference can be an integral part of an employee's career development plan (see Chapter 10), but effort should be made to spread attendance among as many employees as possible.

Professional associations often provide other opportunities for continuing education through regional meetings and workshops and online offerings. One resource for identifying radiologic continuing education courses is www.RADLIST.com.

Public Seminars

It is a rare professional or manager who does not regularly receive brochures announcing seminars on everything from telephone skills to power negotiating. This multimillion dollar business thrives by offering primarily 1 and 2 day courses in major cities on topics of use to a wide range of working adults. The cost is usually moderate, especially for those living in or near the seminar city. The topics tend to be those most in demand, but they are usually generic and limited to topics currently in vogue. The less expensive the seminar, the larger the number of participants, which decreases the opportunity for interaction or practice sessions.

The literature usually spells out the learning objectives, so the employee and administrator can decide if the seminar meets the needs of the organization. As with professional conference attendance, the value of sending 1 or more employees to a public seminar can be increased by requiring the employee to present key points to coworkers. Also, because these seminars offer little opportunity to practice the skills being taught, the supervisor should provide these opportunities on-the-job as soon after completion of the seminar as possible.

Educational Institutions

Community colleges, business and technical schools, and universities offer opportunities ranging from individual courses to advanced degrees. Many have developed sophisticated online (or distance) learning programs, in addition to their on-campus offerings. Imaging centers and other radiology facilities can encourage employees to pursue these additional educational opportunities by offering a tuition reimbursement program.

A tuition reimbursement program can be an effective recruiting and retention tool, especially for technical and professional employees who are in high demand. The program demonstrates the facility's regard for its employees, some of whom seek positions based at least in part on the availability of training and related reimbursement benefits. A survey by the Society for Human Resource Management found that 85% of US companies offer educational assistance.[8]

The specifics of tuition reimbursement programs vary from industry to industry and organization to organization. However, most have similar eligibility criteria[7]:

- Courses must be offered by accredited organizations.
- Reimbursement is contingent on successful completion of the course.
- Employees attend courses during non-working hours. If courses are attended during work hours, it must be approved.
- Completion of courses leads to a degree, professional certificate, or diploma.

Formal guidelines governing the program should be available at new employee orientation and in the employee handbook. Among the elements to consider are what will be covered (eg, tuition, books, related materials), what level will be covered (eg, full cost or partial), how approval must be obtained, whether courses must be directly work-related, and the maximum level of reimbursement per employee. The program should be available to all employees, flexible enough to allow for unusual circumstances, and subject to annual review.

Managers can encourage employees to use the program by profiling student employees on the facility intranet, on a bulletin board, or in the newsletter; mentioning the program occasionally at staff meetings; and sending out facility wide emails or brochures several weeks before the start of a new term. Usage statistics should be monitored; if units are not using the program or usage declines over previous years, the program administrator should follow up to evaluate the need for changes. As a way to get additional value from the investment, employees can be encouraged to use actual work situations for class projects and to share information and skills learned with their coworkers.

On-the-Job Training

By some estimates, as much as 75% of training in the United States takes place on-the-job, including both formal and informal situations.[6] Any employee may need training to correct a deficiency or apply a newly identified best practice. Most informal training is carried out as part of the coaching process, as discussed in Chapter 12, often in a just-in-time fashion.

In addition, even the most skilled new employee will need training in procedures and processes specific to the facility, which may be carried out in a more formal fashion. For example, a newly hired technologist might be assigned to work in a general room for a day or more with an experienced staff member, who will train the new employee to use the room following department approved routines and safety procedures. This would include the use of department systems, such as computed radiography, the picture archiving and communications system (PACS), and the radiology information system (RIS). As the training occurs, each element of the training should be checked off on a competency form designed specifically for that piece of equipment. Once competencies are proven, the new employee may then begin performing procedures on his or her own in this room without supervision. Competency check sheets should be completed for all of the imaging equipment that will be operated, as well as positioning aids such as Pigg-O-Stats, contrast material injectors, information systems, and all medical equipment. See Box 9.6 for sample competency check sheet.

Successful on-the-job training shares many of the same elements as other types of training programs. Supervisors and others responsible for the training should receive training themselves in adult learning principles, techniques, and content organization. In addition, if more than 1 person takes on training responsibilities for the same task(s), every effort should be made to standardize how all trainers carry out and teach the task.

Box 9.6 Sample Competency Check Sheet

PEDIATRIC CHEST RADIOGRAPH WITH PIGG-O-STAT UNIT				
TECHNOLOGIST:				
REVIEWED BY: DATE:	Y	N		COMMENTS
Explained procedure to parent or guardian				
Secured lead apron on parent or guardian				
Turned tube from vertical to horizontal in safe manner				
Aligned Pigg-O-Stat 72" from x-ray tube				
Selected proper patient size holder on unit				
Adjusted seat, if necessary				
Carefully and safely place child in Pigg-O-Stat facing away from tube with arms up				
Explained to parents/guardian reason for holding child's arms up during exam, closed holders around the child				
Secured child's head with the leather strap				
Secured child's body with the holder clips at base of unit				
Selected proper film size for procedure				
Properly placed film in film holder on unit				
Properly positioned the film to the child's chest (for PA and lateral view)				
Removed unwanted, potential artifacts from area of interest				
Identified the film with "R", "L," and other appropriate lead marker identification				
Properly used gonadal shielding				
Aligned tube and central ray to the center of the film				
Coned or collimated to the part of interest				
Selected correct technical factors at the control panel				
Made exposures on full inspiration				
Gently turned child and holder 90° to the left lateral position while the parent/guardian held the child's arms up				

Source: Santa Clara Valley Medical Center, San Jose, CA.

One or more training objectives should be set, along with some form of benchmark or evaluation. Lesson plans or at least a content outline should be created, again to help standardize instruction and to guide the supervisors/trainers.

The process for training an employee on-the-job should include 4 steps that broadly mimic those of more formal training workshops:

1. The first step is to briefly explain the task to be learned, the reason(s) it needs to be done, and how the employee should do it.
2. Next, the trainer should demonstrate how the task should be done. For complex tasks, the process should be broken up into simpler modules and taught in sections.
3. The employee then carries out the task with the trainer observing. This provides the opportunity for positive feedback as well as corrections.
4. Once the employee begins to carry out the task unsupervised, the trainer should check back from time to time to provide additional feedback, answer questions, and make sure the training objectives have been met.

Evaluating a Training Program

In addition to the direct cost of training (eg, workshop fees, consultant fees, or material costs), a facility also incurs considerable indirect cost, particularly from lost productivity for employees who are in the classroom rather than on-the-job. Furthermore, employees can become demotivated after taking part in training which is pereceived as wasting their time or leaves them more confused than before the session. Performing evaluations at several levels will help establish the effectiveness of the training and its value to the organization and build a case for future training as well.

As noted earlier, *The Trainer's Tool Kit* by Cy Charney and Kathy Conway suggests 4 levels of evaluation: the trainee's evaluation of the training, an evaluation of the trainee's understanding of the concepts (short term), an evaluation of the degree to which the trainee is applying the training on-the-job, and an evaluation of the quantifiable results (longer term).[7]

New employees undergoing orientation and any employee taking part in formal training should be asked to complete an evaluation of the session before returning to their jobs (see Box 9.7). Programs should be evaluated on content, presentation methods, and the skill and patience of the instructors. When relevant, participants should also be asked to evaluate the circumstances under which training took place (eg, the facilities). The form should be simple to use and incorporate opportunities for trainees to not only provide numerical ratings, but also comments. Time should be provided at the end of the training for completion of the forms.

Box 9.7 Sample Preceptor Evaluation Form

Please evaluate your preceptor in the following areas below. This will help us improve our orientation process. Please feel free to address any areas of concern that you may have.

Preceptor:_____

	Met Expectations	Did Not Meet Expectations
Do you feel that your preceptor was knowledgeable about your area's processes (including policies and procedures)?		
Do you feel that you were treated with dignity and respect?		
Were your anxieties and concerns addressed in a professional manner?		
Was your orientation organized and completed in a timely manner?		
Did the orientation meet your needs?		
Were you taught to work as a team member?		
Did the preceptor present the orientation to you in a positive manner?		
Do you feel you were informed of changes in the orientation schedule and what was expected of you for that day?		
Did the preceptor prepare you to function independently?		
Would you recommend this person to perform as a preceptor in the future?		

Additional Comments:

_____

_____

_____

_____

_____

Signature: _____

Date:_____

Director: _____

Date:_____

Source: Middle Tennessee Medical Center, Murfreesboro, TN.

Of course, evaluating the course tells the manager nothing about whether the training was effective. The other 3 levels of evaluation are designed to accomplish that. Unless the trainee truly understands the key concepts, he or she is unlikely to successfully apply them to the job. Usually, the evaluation of understanding is a 2 step process involving a pre-test and post-test based on the attitudes, skills, and/or knowledge the training is intended to change. Charney and Conway recommend carrying out the post-test, which may be pencil and paper or a simulation, 2 to 3 months after the training and, if possible, to give it also to employees who did not complete the training but are expected to perform in a similar fashion.[7] A comparison of the results for the 2 groups will be a gauge of the training's effectiveness.

About 6 months after the training takes place, an evaluation should take place to determine whether trainees have actually been applying their new skills, attitudes, or knowledge on-the-job. A 360 degree feedback process (Chapter 11) involving the trainee, supervisor, and selected coworkers is one method; a second is to review relevant productivity reports for the periods before and after the training. If the training was designed to change attitudes (affective learning), effectiveness can be evaluated indirectly, by observing and measuring behaviors such as increased community involvement through the facility, reduced interpersonal conflict, fewer patient complaints, decreased rates of absenteeism and turnover, and reduced error rates.[6]

Finally, the results and their impact on the bottom line and the organization need to be assessed in a process similar to cost-benefit analysis. Because training is focused on achieving change, this level of evaluation seeks to determine whether that change has indeed occurred. Three to 12 months after the training, the manager can use the learning objectives as guides for what changes to look for and calculate how much training time and money were needed to achieve the change and, when possible, how much has been saved. Have patient complaints related to the reception staff declined by 75% and, if so, what was the cost (time and money) to achieve that result? Have repeat mammogram rates declined by the desired level, what was the cost to achieve this change, and what savings did it achieve? For hard to evaluate affective learning, the results of the second level of evaluation described above can be assessed in terms of the costs.

Conclusion

Most employees realize that lifetime learning is essential to enable them to adapt to change, earn competitive salaries, and remain in the workplace throughout their working life. Employers who provide these learning opportunities reap the benefits with workers who are skilled, motivated, and able to think and adapt when needed. Training begins in the interview process, as a potential employee is introduced to the mission and values of the organization and to the expectations for the specific job. Orientation of newly hired employees continues the learning process and provides them with a sound foundation from which to build their careers with the facility. In a field such as healthcare, which is based on the skills and attitudes of the people who serve the patients, on-the-job and formal training and continuing education opportunities are crucial for a facility to maintain its competitive edge and achieve high levels of customer service and patient care.

References

1. Cadwell CM. *New Employee Orientation: a Practical Guide for Supervisors.* Menlo Park, CA: Crisp Publications, Inc.; 1988.

2. Brown J. Employee orientation: keeping new employees on board! Available at: http://www.humanlinks.com/manres/articles/employee_orientation.htm. Accessed October 14, 2006.

3. Kelly Scientific Resources. Building an effective orientation program. Available at: http://www.kellyscientific.us/web/us/ksr/en/pages/build_orientation_program.html. Accessed October 23, 2006.

4. Jerris LA. *Effective Employee Orientation.* New York, NY: American Management Association; 1993.

5. Platz B. Employee onboarding: one chance for a positive new employee experience. Available at: http://humanresources.about.com/od/orientation/a/onboarding.htm. Accessed October 14, 2006.

6. Mitchell G. *The Trainer's Handbook: the AMA Guide to Effective Training.* 3rd ed. New York, NY: American Management Association; 1998.

7. Charney C, Conway K. *The Trainer's Tool Kit.* New York, NY: American Management Association; 1998.

8. Arthur D. *The Employee Recruitment and Retention Handbook.* New York, NY: American Management Association; 2001.

Chapter 10

Career Development

Roberta M. Edge

> In this chapter, talent management and employee engagement, which are related to successful organizational career development, and the significance of an individual's responsibility for one's own career development will be discussed. The use of career ladders for clinical staff is addressed, as is succession planning within an organization to develop current and future leaders.

The imaging profession offers an abundance of opportunities for life long career growth. Imaging technologists find work in various sized community hospitals, academic medical centers, freestanding imaging centers, radiologists' practices, breast centers, or in multispecialty physician groups. The road to management can begin as a shift supervisor in a hospital. Many imaging administrators began their careers as technologists. Others who have a business only background are directors of radiologists' practices, some have become "C" level professionals (eg, chief operating officer) by pursuing advanced degrees in administration, and still others have used their clinical backgrounds to become account representatives or applications specialists for various vendors of the products and equipment used to produce images for patients.

In choosing one of the many paths available to imaging professionals within an organization, it is paramount to take into account the needs of the organization. Imaging administrators are recognizing the value of developing future leaders within their organizations, as well as promoting career development programs for technologists and other staff members in their organizations. See Sidebar 10.1 for career development key points.

Organizational Needs and Career Assessment

Healthcare organizations engage in strategic planning to "define their organizational objectives, implement strategies to achieve those objectives and measure the effectiveness of those strategies."[1] Included in those organizational objectives are recruiting and retaining the right professionals to keep an organization viable in today's healthcare market. In healthcare organizations that include an imaging department, an imaging center, or a radiologists' practice, people are the most valuable asset, key

---

SIDEBAR 10.1: Career Development Key Points

- People are any organization's most valuable asset.
- Align individual talent with business needs.
- Individual employees should update resumes annually.
- Engaged employees are emotionally and intellectually committed to an organization.
- Credibility, connection, and contribution keep employees engaged.
- Career development programs include training, access to information, performance appraisal, and career paths.
- Career development is up to the individual to carry out.
- In the imaging industry, excellent technical skills do not necessarily translate to excellent leadership skills.
- Leadership development is an ongoing commitment of an organization and the individual.
- The imaging leader's role is to motivate and inspire staff, develop skills, and provide access to tools for growth.

---

to the success of the organization especially when there is a shortage of technologists, radiologists, and imaging administrators. State-of-the-art equipment can be purchased and installed, but if there is no staff to operate the equipment or radiologists to interpret the images, then there is no practice.

Most imaging facilities strive for the same business objectives: exceptional customer service, high quality services, and rapid report turnaround time to referring providers. To accomplish these objectives, imaging administrators must have a plan to allow current employees to assess their career objectives. Knowledge of the vision of the organization is essential so that resources unavailable from within the organization can be recruited elsewhere.

A good time to assist employees in assessing how one's career is progressing is during an annual evaluation. Questions during that encounter to be discussed are: What career goals and objectives will be met this year, and in the long term? How do the individual's plans fit with the needs of the organization and/or profession? This is also the time to add any significant accomplishments to one's resume, such as publications, awards, completion of projects, obtaining advanced certification or being awarded an academic degree.

Talent Management

The Society of Human Resource Management (SHRM) defines *talent* as an attribute of "any individuals who have the capability to make a significant difference to the current and future performance of the company," and defines *talent management* as "the implementation of integrated strategies or systems designed to increase

---

workplace productivity by developing improved processes for attracting, developing, retaining, and utilizing people with the required skills and aptitude to meet current and future business needs."[2]

In the imaging field, talent management requires the careful examination of the skill sets of all staff members, with a view toward the needs of the organization with the talents and aptitudes of staff to develop a more competitive service. Mature staff will retire and other staff will leave the organization to pursue other interests or opportunities; therefore, administrators are wise to look within their ranks to find staff with high potential to fill the void, and then mentor, train, and develop these individuals.

As an example, one of the hardest positions to fill in imaging is the sonographer. Ultrasonography is a growing area for diagnosis and treatment in many aspects of healthcare. Since the business strategy is to grow ultrasonography and the business need is to have well trained, competent sonographers to perform studies, an important professional development avenue open to the organization is to sponsor an individual who meets the requirements for sonography school and has the desire to learn a new modality through the training program. The administrator identifies the talent and then manages the outcome through training.

Employee Engagement

Before a successful career development plan can be implemented, employees who will participate must be engaged in the organization. When employees speak positively about an organization, have an intense desire to belong to an organization, and exert effort to help the organization succeed, they are said to be engaged (ie, emotionally and intellectually committed to the organization).[3] Imaging has been dealing with a staffing shortage of technologists, radiologists, and leaders since the beginning of the 21st century. Although some geographic areas report this shortage easing, there is a large potential for loss of talent through retirement as the Baby Boom generation begins to leave the workforce in record numbers over the course of the next 20 years. The Associated Press reported the first Baby Boomer applied for Social Security on October 16, 2007, and expects approximately 10,000 people per day to be applying for retirement over the next 20 years.[4]

Engaging the employees already retained by an organization requires attention to their individual needs and connecting those needs to the organization. For example, more mature workers may extend their employment when offered the opportunity to work fewer days per week, or to take a per diem status while still drawing their retirement benefits. This gives that employee a certain amount of control over their time spent at work, provides a balance between home and work life, and continues to provide a social network. Each of these attributes will enhance the loyalty and trust of that particular employee with the organization, and will demonstrate to others the commitment of the organization to employees. Credibility, connection, and contribution are all points that enhance the goal of engaging employees in an organization.[3]

Career Development Programs

Once employees are engaged, a career development program can be designed and implemented. The strategic plan of the organization needs to be referenced to determine the expertise, education, and skills needed to reach the organizational goals of the company, then assessing what talent already resides in the organization, which positions have transferable skills to higher level positions, and what positions will most likely be needed in the future as the organization grows (see Chapter 2). The purpose of a career development program is to link business objectives to employee goals.[5]

Successful career development programs share common ingredients. They might include training (internal and external), access to information on labor market conditions, performance appraisals, career pathing (ie, how employees can move from their current positions to a higher one), mentoring, tuition reimbursement, and supervisory or management specific training. Also, a career development program can benefit from exit interviews, which help determine why employees are leaving the organization.[5]

With use of the aforementioned tools, actual career development is up to the individual employee. Administrators can help each individual by writing up a plan with the employee, taking time to monitor progress, and making career development goals part of the annual performance appraisal.[6] Mentoring is a tool that individuals can use to enhance any program developed between an employer and employee. If the administrator is the original mentor, steps can be taken to keep in touch with these individuals long after they have moved on to their new position, and encourage them to develop the same type of mentoring relationship with the new superior (see Chapter 12). Networking is also an important tool. Through professional associations, individuals can develop an extensive network with colleagues they feel can enhance their career development and long term goals.

Examples of Career Development

An example of utilizing a career development plan could be a clerical supervisor (an imaging administrator's direct report) who expresses interest during her annual performance evaluation in becoming an imaging administrator. She currently has a bachelor's degree in business management with an information technology focus. She has never been a technologist and is aware of the underlying bias of organizations that clinical managers "should" have clinical experience before entering into management of a clinical department. She has eagerly taken on learning the picture archiving and communication system (PACS) to assist the PACS coordinator, assists the radiologists in making their weekly tumor board presentations with PowerPoint, and has gained the trust of staff, radiologists, her immediate supervisor, and administration. She has been identified as talented and has budding leadership skills. The imaging administrator over 4 years' time has given her projects, each with more responsibility than the one just completed, and most recently involved her in an organizational service excellence initiative. The clerical supervisor took on the task of managing the disparate information systems in the organization that impact billing of imaging services and has been promoted to business manager. She has begun the process of obtaining her master's degree in business and is on track for becoming an imaging administrator in the next 5 years. Unless the current imaging administrator is promoted, this employee may have to seek that opportunity within the organization but outside of this particular imaging department.

In turn, this clerical supervisor who became the business manager has also provided a career development plan for one of her employees. The imaging clerk has a desire for a career in marketing and wants to stay in healthcare. Her supervisor has adjusted the employee's schedule over the past 3 years so the employee can complete her bachelor's degree in business with an emphasis in marketing. As this employee gets closer to her graduation, her supervisor has introduced her to the regional vice president of marketing, and spoken to the chief operating officer about this employee. The organization is actively growing its marketing department, so the time is ripe for this employee to finish her degree and move on to another department in the same organization with more opportunity for growth and development of her career.

Of all the staff members employed in an imaging facility, perhaps the person in the best position to easily use a career development plan is the technologist. Technologists generally are trained in radiography whether in a hospital-based or community college-based program, and then may seek advanced certification in mammography, computed tomography (CT), or magnetic resonance imaging (MRI). Of course, not all facilities require MRI technologists to have been radiologic technologists.

There are some bachelor degree programs in radiology, though these are not as common as hospital or community college programs. With further training, imaging technologists and other allied health professionals can become sonographers and could be certified by the American Registry of Diagnostic Medical Sonographers. Nuclear medicine is a separate track of training and licensure. Many states require state certification, some giving reciprocity for national registry, whereas others require their own method of testing. Please refer to individual state's department of health services for specific information.

Clinical Ladders

Clinical ladders are developed by organizations to reduce turnover, increase retention, improve staff satisfaction and morale, and provide a path to career growth and job enrichment and, as a byproduct, increase one's salary.[7]

Multiple modalities lend themselves to a clinical ladder, part of the career development plan upon which the organization and the individual technologists can build. Having several technologists who are competent in multiple modalities allows for better coverage of services for the organization. The technologists are more marketable and are more valuable to the organization with multiple competencies. Some clinical ladders require proven competency as well as certification in each modality and take years of experience into account. Proven customer service skills, community service, and letters of recommendation can also be factors that are key for advancement.

When clinical ladders are developed, it is essential to use a team consisting of technologists, radiologists, administrators, human resource professionals, and imaging educators. The team will determine the qualifications, goals, outcomes, and processes for moving to the next rung in the ladder. Most clinical ladders use a fixed percentage in salary increase between each level in the ladder, generally 3% to 10% per level.[7]

Clerical roles in an imaging facility are changing as digital technology advances. Fully digital departments no longer require film librarians or film hangers. These skills are transferable to image management in the digital world. Film hangers know the radiologists' preferences for viewing images and can be taught to enter relevant prior films into a digitizer to allow for comparisons in PACS. Film librarians can learn to burn CDs for shipment outside the department and to manage electronic patient files rather than paper files.

Management roles require further education beyond any imaging services skills. At this writing, virtually all employers require a bachelor's degree in business or health administration, along with years of clinical training to become an imaging administrator or imaging practice manager. The more complex the organization, the more likely a master's degree will be required. Many organizations will not require any clinical background if a candidate has a demonstrated track record in business, as imaging services generates a large portion of the revenue. Some smaller facilities may require a clinical background, as one of the expectations of the imaging manager may be to perform imaging procedures.

When pursuing higher education, many are attracted to online degree programs because they can be completed in off hours and do not require travel to and from a university. The drawback to these programs is the lack of dialogue and face-to-face interaction provided in a conventional degree program. However, there are degree programs that will integrate both online and face-to-face interaction. Regardless of which degree is undertaken, be sure it is accredited and the curriculum offered will provide the didactic information necessary for the management position being sought. Higher education is critical as the world of imaging services becomes more complex in that it helps to develop critical thinking and problem solving skills. Students pursuing advanced degrees report an ability to ask better questions, the development of strategic thinking and planning, and learning how imaging fits into an entire organization.[8]

Succession Planning

Many talented leaders and staff in the Baby Boomer generation will be retiring in the next 3 to 15 years. Companies need to evaluate succession planning and look at individuals within their organization to fill these vacancies by doing formal assessments of skills, current abilities, and potential for development. One method that can be used is a matrix that measures results and behaviors and then places the individual in 1 of 9 boxes on the matrix (see Table 10.1). Individuals rated in the top row with high ratings in performance results and who display behaviors such as teamwork, leadership skills, interpersonal skills, and customer service, are identified as employees who need "further development in current position" (upper left hand box), are "ready for promotion within the department" (middle box), or are "ready for promotion within the facility or the company at large" (upper right hand box). These employees are then invited to participate in a career development plan designed to help them achieve their career goals.

A career development program lends itself readily to succession planning on all levels of an organization. Progressive organizations know that key management positions such as imaging administrator require thoughtful consideration as to who will lead the department for the foreseeable future. One of the 3 major mistakes organizations make with professional development is promoting from within.[9] Organizations spend human and financial resources in developing talent and

Table 10.1

RESULTS		Uses Ineffective Behaviors	Uses Effective Behaviors Consistently	Exceptionally Applies Effective Behaviors
	Exceeds Expected Results	*Exceeds Expected Results* *Uses Ineffective Behaviors* **Further development in current position**	*Exceeds Expected Results* *Uses Effective Behaviors Consistently* **Ready for promotion within department**	*Exceeds Expected Results* *Exceptionally Applies Effective Behaviors* **Ready for promotion outside department (within facility or company)**
	Consistently Meets Expected Results	Consistently Meets Expected Results Uses Ineffective Behaviors	Consistently Meets Expected Results Uses Effective Behaviors Consistently	Consistently Meets Expected Results Exceptionally Applies Effective Behaviors
	Does Not Meet Expected Results	Does Not Meet Expected Results Uses Ineffective Behaviors	Does Not Meet Expected Results Uses Effective Behaviors Consistently	Does Not Meet Expected Results Exceptionally Applies Effective Behaviors
		Uses Ineffective Behaviors	Uses Effective Behaviors Consistently	Exceptionally Applies Effective Behaviors

BEHAVIORS

therefore may feel compelled to place people who are developed into positions of greater responsibility. Leaders are actually perceived as more effective when coming from outside an organization than when promoted from within. When organizations develop talent, the focus is to develop talent for the profession and the healthcare industry at large, not necessarily for the current employer. However, many organizations have a culture of promoting from within and do so very successfully. These organizations value the long term relationship of employees moving from entry level positions to those of leadership over the course of time. Time to obtain higher education, tuition assistance, and internal mentoring are methods used to support engaged employees who show the desire and self-motivation to grow within an organization.

At the level of imaging administrator, one rarely encounters candidates who do not have the technical skills or knowledge to do the job. The most often cited reason a candidate is not selected is being perceived as "not a good fit" for the organization. Questions posed to the candidates for leadership roles should draw out how the person fits culturally with the organization. When candidates spend time researching the culture of the organization they are considering employment with, they may save themselves time by applying for positions where they know their personal values and leadership style will not be at odds with those of the organization. Whether the organization looks at candidates from inside or outside the organization, the aforementioned qualities of flexibility, critical thinking skills, and emotional intelligence should be considered when selecting a candidate.

Leadership

"The ideal leader is flexible, proactive, possesses strategic thinking and analytical skills, is culturally competent and adept at competitive positioning."[10] Add to these qualities emotional intelligence, defined as a "heightened sense of self-awareness, the ability to manage their emotions and the emotions of others, to build rapport and relationships with a diverse group of people, to motivate others, to create a believable vision and to negotiate a broad range of social and business situations,"[11] and one has the potential to be a good leader.

Traditionally in the imaging industry, the best technologist has been promoted into leadership roles. However, excellent technical skills do not necessarily translate into the qualities and expertise needed for a leadership role. The personal desire and interest in becoming a leader, the drive to make a positive difference in the organization, and the willingness to take on responsibility will more likely result in the development of an effective leader.[12]

Leadership development is an ongoing commitment of an organization with formal and informal training to develop and enhance leadership skills and styles. It encompasses how quickly the organization needs to move forward, what are considered effective leadership methods in the organization, the investment of time and money, and a demonstration of successful leadership methods.[10] Leadership development may start with a program, but to be effective needs to continue past the half day seminar. Each leader is assessed for all competencies he or she brings—motives, values, traits, self-image, technical skills, behaviors, and knowledge—and the effective use of 6 leadership styles: coercive, authoritative, affiliative, democratic, pacesetting, and coaching. Awareness of how leadership style creates climate and how that climate ultimately affects performance and customer service are also critical.[11]

Successful, high performing organizations use a process for leadership development. The process includes assessment of individuals, as indicated in a Hay Group study (the Hay Group is a global management consultancy that uses research data to help their clients develop effective organizations; one of many research studies they have conducted and used to guide their clients is on leadership development), as well as customizing competency-driven models that support the organization's strategic goals. This process goes on to expand the emotional intelligence of the individuals, provides extensive coaching, and finally has measurable development milestones with explicit rewards for performance.[10]

Professional associations can also be a source for developing leadership skills (see Sidebar 10.2). Many offer presentations at their annual meetings on methods to develop skills as an individual. Some offer mentoring opportunities that involve applying for a scholarship to be placed with a more experienced professional. Still others develop certifications and publications to assist their members in developing leadership skills.

Conclusion

Imaging administrators working in concert with the organization employing them can influence the process of career development for themselves and their employees. A cornerstone is personal responsibility once the process is established and a commitment to the profession. The imaging leader's job is to motivate and inspire the frontline staff members who care for patients each day, look for skills and qualities in each of those individuals, and provide access to tools for growth.

References

1. Zuckerman A. *Healthcare Strategic Planning Approaches for the 21st Century.* Chicago, IL: Foundation of the American College of Healthcare Executives; 1998.

2. Lockwood NR. Talent management: overview. 2005. Available at: http://www.shrm.org/research/briefly_published/Talent%20Management%20Series%20Pa. Accessed April 10, 2007.

3. Lockwood NR. Employee engagement. 2005. Available at: http://www.shrm.org/research/briefly_published/Talent%20Management%20Series%20Pa. Accessed April 10, 2007.

4. Cox News Service. First baby boomer applies for Social Security. 2007. Associated Press. Available at: http://www.detnews.com/apps/pbcs.dll/article?AID=/20071016/POLITICS/710160340/1022. Accessed November 12, 2007.

5. Prochaska ST. *Designing Organizational Programs for Employee Career Development.* Alexandria, VA: Society for Human Resource Management; 2000 (reviewed 2002).

6. Society for Human Resource Management. Career development. 2006. Available at: http://www.shrm.org/hrresources/basic_published/CMS_002768.asp. Accessed April 10, 2007.

7. Wall M. Developing and implementing a career ladder program. *Radiol Manage* 2007;29:42–49.

8. Edge R. Pursuing advanced degrees. AHRA. *Link.* 2003;22(1).

9. Varnavas MJ. Capture the benefits of professional development. AHRA. *Link.* 2006;25(7).

10. Lockwood NR. Leadership development. 2005. Available at: http://www.shrm.org/research/briefly_published/Talent%20Management%20Series%20Pa. Accessed April 10, 2007.

11. The Hay Group. What makes leaders great: rethinking the route to effective leadership. 1999. Available at: http://www.haygroup.com. Accessed April 10, 2007.

12. Edge R. Succession planning: not just for CEO's. AHRA. *Link.* 2003;22(4).

Chapter 11

Appraise and Improve Performance

Ed Yoder

An integrated performance management system is an invaluable tool to drive employee performance and achieve the organization's goals. The system includes training and assessment, as discussed in Chapter 10; performance appraisals, discussed in this chapter; and ongoing coaching, feedback, and mentoring, as discussed in Chapter 12. Among the types of appraisal systems are essays, rating scales, and management by objectives, each of which has its advantages and disadvantages. All types incorporate an appraisal interview, for which both the manager and the employee should prepare to conduct as a collaboration, primarily as a planning session for future performance.

In too many organizations for too many years, performance appraisals have seemed like annual torture for both managers and their employees. Managers often had little or no training in how to effectively conduct an appraisal and would put off the task as long as possible. In some cases, their appraisals were influenced more by an employee's congeniality than performance and, too often, fear, laziness, or lack of training led to nearly all employees receiving the same "acceptable" rating, especially if pay increases were tied to the appraisal. Employees may have thought their manager did not understand what they did and so could not possibly carry out a fair and accurate appraisal. The sessions could turn into a gripe session or involve little more than listening to the manager list what the employee has done wrong since the last appraisal.

However, businesses that recognize how crucial employee performance is to the organization's success have also recognized that when the performance appraisal is integrated into an entire performance management system, the appraisal becomes a valuable tool for both the manager and the employee. This is a process that includes providing training and assessments to match an employer's career goals with the organization's needs and ongoing coaching, feedback, and mentoring.

Many imaging facilities, especially large centers with a fully staffed human resource department, will have a performance appraisal process in place, including timelines, procedures, and forms. Nevertheless, many of the techniques discussed in this chapter may be applicable to various appraisal processes.

Employees want to do well in their jobs, and they want to feel that they are rewarded for their performance. They want to know they have done well and how they can achieve their individual goals within the organizational culture. Developing these employee behaviors will depend on the organization's culture, mission, and values. These factors need to be tied into the performance appraisal and the performance management system of the organization.

Developing a performance management system is a crucial part of performance planning within the medical imaging facility. Having a well thought out plan gives all parties involved the criteria and expectations of the system. Knowing what is expected in job performance has a significant impact on employee satisfaction, which in turn leads to better employee retention.

Qualities of Effective Performance Management Systems

Several factors have significant impact on the success of performance management systems:

- Clear performance criteria and standards that are related to the job and are communicated clearly at the point of hire and when circumstances change
- Adequately trained managers who nurture adequately trained employees
- An integrated appraisal system that provides continuous measurement and feedback
- Developmental activities that occur throughout the year to correct poor performance and build on good or great performance
- Appraisals based on job-related behaviors and results rather than personal characteristics
- Formulation of plans to correct poor performance and to build on good performances in the future

Clear performance criteria and standards related to job performance should be made known during the initial hire and orientation period and then detailed again in each performance appraisal. At the point of hire, employees should understand the behavior expectation and job performance standards they will be held to and expected to fulfill. This helps build a referral base for the ongoing feedback of job performance that occurs throughout the year, streamlining expectations and making the review portion of the year end performance evaluation a year end summary.

Imaging administrators and other managers must be trained on the best ways to give feedback and train employees appropriately and on how to carry out effective performance appraisals. Detailing expectations at the point of hire makes feedback conversations easier, but it does not eliminate the need for managers to be trained in effective listening, displaying empathy, and communicating clearly and, when necessary, forcefully. They must be trained to handle difficult discussions. Every healthcare organization needs to invest in manager training to develop a good performance feedback and evaluation program. The reward is a well-functioning unit and increased employee satisfaction and employee retention.

The performance appraisal tool should be designed to continuously measure performance with mechanisms for built in feedback. The manager should develop the appraisal to measure desired behaviors that help achieve departmental and organizational goals. Feedback to each employee on performance should be measurable and consistent throughout the overall evaluation period. Task measurements should be specific, measurable, achievable, realistic, and time oriented.

Developmental activities that occur during the appraisal year should build on good performance and correct poor performance at the time it occurs. Waiting until the annual performance evaluation to remedy these issues will leave employees confused because they may not remember the incident or issue. Delays will also leave them with feelings of helplessness or anger because the employees may have been led to believe their performance was fine or even excellent. Timely training may shorten the learning curve because the employee sees a direct connection between training and job performance, and it gives the employee time to implement new skills or behaviors before the annual review.

All components of the performance appraisal system should focus on job-related behaviors and expectations, not personal characteristics (see Box 11.1). This helps ensure that all employees are assessed fairly, equitably, rationally, and without bias. First, the critical performance criteria should be identified for each output; for instance, a critical criterion output for quality could be accuracy, or low repeat rates. A critical criterion for productivity may be the output produced per hour with accuracy. Finally, a critical criterion for cost may be efficiently using supplies and materials. Once the critical criteria are identified, a standardized measurement for each critical output must be developed that can be applied to all similar or like employees. In the quality example above, if accuracy is the critical output for an imaging technologist position, then the measurement should answer the question, "What is an acceptable accuracy rate?" Referring to industry standards or historical data for the facility will usually provide useful rates. Once the rate has been determined, it becomes the benchmark for that job-related behavior.

Finally, the measurements should lead to a performance standard or expectations that influence employee goals for each measure. With regard to quality, for example, once the repeat rate has been established, an appropriate departmental and/or employee goal might be that all repeat rates are above the established benchmark figure.

The final element in a good performance management system is the plans that are formulated to correct poor performance and to build on good performance in the future. Improvement plans should be an integral part of the performance management system and should monitor the performance and give feedback until poor performance achieves standards or the employee leaves or is terminated. The focus should not be on the negative; however, as the behavior changes, the corrected performance must be recognized within the performance management system to allow for growth and further employee development.

Feedback: Prelude to a Performance Appraisal Session

As discussed in greater detail in Chapter 12, in the context of employee development, feedback is information related to a certain performance. Effective feedback is usually immediate, occurring when or shortly after a behavior happens. It is generally verbal. Employees tend to see properly given feedback as being neutral and nonthreatening and often view it in a positive light, even if it aims to correct or change behavior.

Frequent feedback provides opportunities to discuss quality issues and varying performance. By providing feedback, the manager is opening the dialogue for 2 way communication between the manager and employee. These conversations can help managers see how they may be constructing barriers to the employee's development. The best way to find solutions to problems is to work on them in collaboration.

By managing the feedback given to an employee, the manager corrects or rewards behaviors in small doses over time before issues become a crisis. This takes less time for both the employee and the manager. Staffing and performance issues can consume a large portion of a manager's time. Effectively managing these issues can reduce the workload and stress that is involved with these situations. Employees become less hostile and are more prepared for the year end performance appraisal if they are properly prepared with consistent and steady feedback.

When feedback is consistently discussed, it builds a mechanism of trust between employees and their managers. The employees begin to see their managers as sounding boards and confidantes and can then begin to trust them and their ability to help build employees' skill. Once this bridge has been constructed, it becomes easier to face and discuss more substantial barriers to performance. Frequency is again the key, capturing a behavior—good or bad—when it happens makes it easier to discuss the parameters and behaviors involved and makes correcting or rewarding behaviors at the point of occurrence that much easier.

Performance feedback must be continuous and frequent. It is important that the employee knows that the formal performance appraisal is only a small part of the overall performance management plan. Without feedback, the performance appraisal alone will not improve an employee's job performance.[1] A continuous thread runs from the development plan to measurement, to feedback, to development, and then back to the appraisal. Each year, the performance management system comes back to planning and the cycle runs over again.

The annual performance appraisal gives the manager and employee an opportunity to discuss the year's performance and evaluate it on a predetermined scale. However, the end result should be no surprise to employees because the frequent feedback sessions have laid the groundwork for the annual performance appraisal and the items discussed really then become a year in review for employees. Most important, goals for the next year are usually set and should coincide with the overall organizational goals of the facility or department.

Qualities of Effective Performance Appraisals

In her book, *Powerful Performance Appraisals*, Karen McKirchy refers to the formal performance appraisal as a "conversation that gets somewhere. It has objectives, an orderly track, and results in concrete agreements."[2] If conducted effectively, the appraisal should do the following[3]:

- Provide feedback on results as they relate to the individual employee
- Motivate employees to perform better by carrying out specified behaviors
- Reveal development opportunities not only to improve future performance, but also enhance the employee's career options

- Distinguish high performing employees from substandard ones
- Provide documentation for performance-based termination
- Clarify expectations for the job and the employee's performance
- Promote communication between manager and employee

Of course, the performance appraisal is also a legal document that becomes part of the employee's permanent human resource file. As such, it must meet its own set of standards that ensure that it is job-related; based on a thorough analysis of the job; standardized for all employees; free of bias against race, religion, sex, nationality, or sexual preference; and performed by someone who has adequate knowledge of the employee and the job. See Sidebar 11.1 for legal pitfalls in performance appraisals.

SIDEBAR 11.1: Legal Pitfalls in Performance Appraisals

Performance appraisals are an important component of an employee's development, but they are also legal documents that may be read in a court. To reduce potential problems, the manager should avoid any of the following items when conducting an appraisal:

- Predictions about the employee's future with the organization
- Promises about continued employment
- Reassurances that the employee's job is secure
- Predictions of the likelihood of a promotion
- Omissions of issues related to performance to avoid an unpleasant or potentially upsetting discussion
- Omissions of issues related to performance that will support disciplinary action in the near future
- Slurs, potentially offensive language, or sexual comments
- Jokes, which might offend or could imply a less than serious attitude toward the meeting
- Feedback that is nonspecific or related to the employee's personal characteristics
- Criticism that the employee is different from other employees or doesn't fit in
- Undocumented negative feedback, particularly to an employee who has been difficult to work with or has filed a complaint about violations of workplace law (harassment, etc)
- Comments or feedback related to the employee's religion, race, disability, or other "protected" characteristics

Once the written appraisal has been completed, the manager should review the document and ask 2 key questions:

1. "Can I support every statement with documentation or other evidence?"
2. "Does every statement relate to the employee's job performance?"

If not, the statement(s) should be omitted or revised. Human resource staff or the center's legal counsel should be consulted if doubts remain.

Source: DelPo A. *The Performance Appraisal Handbook: Legal & Practical Rules for Managers.* 2nd ed. Berkeley, CA: Nolo; 2007:38–39.

Types of Performance Appraisal Systems

There are many different types of appraisal systems. Imaging administrators and other managers are generally required to work from existing tools and systems used by the organization. The human resource staff usually spends a significant amount of time researching and modifying the performance tool to fit the organization's needs (Box 11.2). However, whereas the human resource staff will select the form and system, the manager must make the measurable criteria fit the job-related tasks. For example, customer service criteria can apply to the receptionist's behavior with patients and the film librarian's behavior with physicians.

The types of systems generally fall within 3 classifications, based on how performance is appraised, with several hybrids: essay, rating scales, and results focused (management by objectives).

Essay Appraisal Systems

As the name indicates, this form of appraisal is based on a written essay. The manager describes the employee's strengths and weaknesses as they relate to job performance and makes suggestions to improve it. The document can be written solely by the supervisor or in collaboration with the employee being appraised.

The primary advantage of this method is its flexibility, especially in comparison to rating scales. The manager can focus on selected skills or performance issues most relevant to the individual employee. The system works especially well when evaluating more qualitative attributes such as patient communication skills or leadership.

However, the flexibility is also a disadvantage. Difficulties arise in comparing and contrasting employees or a given employee from year to year. Opinions and other

---

Box 11.2 Checklist for an Effective Appraisal Form

In many facilities, the human resource staff will be responsible for devising the appraisal form based on the purpose(s) of performance appraisals in the organization (eg, to justify merit raises, to document performance problems, or to support employee development). These elements are most commonly included:

- Objectives set at previous appraisal
- Job description or list of specific skills/competencies to be measured, with examples
- Rating scale with space for comments
- Space for employee self appraisal
- Space for supervisor appraisal essay or specific comments
- Space for suggestions for employee development
- Objectives to be met by next appraisal (or other specified timeframe)

---

subjective evaluation can easily creep into the text with a risk of bias and accusations of unfairness. This format also calls for the ability to write clearly and concisely; a poorly written essay can result in an inaccurate evaluation. Finally, the essay format is time-consuming and difficult for the supervisor to complete. For these reasons, the essay is commonly used in combination with other techniques such as rating scales.

Rating Scales

Rating scales, or behavior checklists, are the most common form of appraisal.[4,5] They consist of a list of job-related behaviors and traits. Each trait is assessed on a scale that varies from a simple 2 prong "satisfactory-unsatisfactory" to a 5 point scale: "outstanding, exceeds standards, meets standards, does not meet standards, and unsatisfactory." Each category is assigned a numerical value, which is tallied to compute the employee's performance score. For example, a 0.1 to 1.0 may be associated with "unsatisfactory," 1.1 to 2.0 to "needs improvement," and 2.1 to 3.0 to "meets standards." In addition, space is usually provided to comment on issues relevant to a specific rating (eg, examples of the employee's behavior that justify an "outstanding" rating or notes about extenuating circumstances that impacted a rating decision).

Generally, employees who rate "outstanding" make continually exceptional, over-the-top contributions to the department. They are key individuals to identify for mentoring and management track positions at some point in their career. They generally have a positive impact on other employees and often coach them. Outstanding employees have mastered all job-related tasks and their behaviors are exemplary; they consistently exceed expectations over several performance appraisals.

Employees who receive a score that places them in the "exceeds expectations" category are generally highly skilled in their job-related tasks, but have some room for continued improvement. They make good coaches to new employees and can be excellent trainers.

Employees who "meet standards" perform their job-related tasks consistently but do not strive for an exceptional performance. They exceed standards in a few categories within the appraisal. These employees show up and perform their job tasks, but need improvement in some areas.

"Does not meet standards" employees are generally team members who repeatedly need help performing their jobs and do not meet all job expectations. They will occasionally demonstrate behaviors that need to be corrected. Their managers will spend a significant amount of time on feedback sessions and implementing corrective measures to modify their behaviors.

"Unsatisfactory" employees consistently underperform and need continual performance correction. These employees are often placed on performance improvement plans and consistently need behavior modification. Their performance appraisal may serve as documentation in support of eventual termination.

Although in theory the application of these categories seems straightforward, in practice, managers have varying interpretations of what constitutes outstanding or other categories of performance. Other disadvantages of rating scales include irrelevance of some traits to a given job, the difficulty in assessing qualitative traits and the difficulty in selecting indicators of performance that accurately and fully reflect the job. Furthermore, as noted earlier, some managers tend to play it safe and give nearly all employees the same rating, usually at the midpoint.

However, rating scales are structured and standardized, and the ratings are easy to compare from year to year or employee to employee. Employees tend to believe they are all being evaluated equally and fairly. Most managers find this system easier and faster to complete, especially compared with essays. Although some employees may object to the idea of being graded on their work, most quickly grasp the numerical score and their ranking because the system mimics that used in most schools.

Management by Objectives

Appraisals based on results, also known as management by objectives, measure performance not by specific behaviors but by results. The actual appraisal is the culmination of a process that begins with setting organizational goals, then working with each employee to set individual and/or team goals and objectives that contribute to their own jobs and to the organizational goals. The appraisal reviews whether goals have been met or exceeded within the predetermined timeframe.

Whereas, historically, management by objectives has been primarily used to evaluate managers and professionals, some organizations have expanded its use to other workers.[5] Its primary advantage is that it focuses on real, observable (or measurable) outcomes. This makes it easy to understand and, to some, it will seem a more accurate and fairer assessment of their performance than trying to evaluate a set of behaviors that may only peripherally relate to their job.

However, the process can be time consuming. Employees and their supervisors must be skilled at accurately evaluating progress toward the objectives. Some employers have found that the system leads to unrealistic expectations about what an employee can and cannot do.[6] Finally, setting and measuring objectives can make employees and the organization rigid and resistant to change, especially if the change will negatively impact achieving an objective.

Carrying Out a Successful Performance Appraisal

No matter what system the imaging facility uses, an effective appraisal has 4 steps: preparation, writing the appraisal, conducting the meeting, and following up.

Preparing for the Appraisal Meeting

As noted at the start of this chapter, performance appraisals are best considered a component of an ongoing process that includes prompt and regular feedback. Although this eliminates surprises for the employee during the performance appraisal, ongoing feedback can also be valuable to the manager when it comes time to prepare an annual review, if incidents that led to feedback are recorded as they happen.

Specifically, DelPo suggests that managers keep a performance log on each employee under their supervision.[1] Kept in the manager's files or on computer (not the employee's personnel file), the log is a simple chart on which notable incidents are recorded—the date, a brief description of the employee's behavior or performance note, and what action, if any, was taken. The log is the place to record compliments or complaints received about an employee; it can include notes about projects completed ahead of schedule, improper use of the facility's computer, or times when the employee worked extra shifts.

In most cases, no one will ever read the performance logs except the manager, so the writing does not need to be perfect. However, as DelPo points out, should an employee sue the facility, the log could become evidence. Therefore, like the appraisal itself, the log should (1) be accurate; (2) include only job-related incidents; (3) avoid slurs, personal comments, or language that could be interpreted as biased or discriminatory; and (4) include specific details.[1]

The performance log will take just 1 to 2 minutes to complete each entry, but it could save hours when it comes time to write an appraisal. The document also helps ensure that employees are evaluated based on the entire year's performance and not just on incidents within recent memory.

About 2 weeks before the meeting, the manager should gather relevant information to write the evaluation draft. These items should include both quantitative data (eg, time sheets) and qualitative material (eg, patient satisfaction survey comments) (Box 11.3).

Box 11.3 Information to Gather for a Performance Appraisal

As with most documents, preparing a performance appraisal will be much easier if relevant documents and records are on hand. Depending on the employee's job classification, items to collect could include:

Reports Detailing Objective Data

- Productivity reports
- Budget reports
- Time and attendance records
- Training and/or continuing education records
- Patient satisfaction survey results

Documentation of Critical Incidents

- Patient complaints or compliments
- Disciplinary notices
- Employee personnel file

Supervisor's Observations

- Performance log
- Notes, emails, and/or telephone messages

Results of Third Party Interviews

- Patients and other customers (eg, physicians, care managers, other departments)
- Coworkers and other managers who are familiar with the employee's work
- Vendors
- Third party payers

Other Job-Related Documents

- Current job description
- Previous performance appraisal
- Results of coaching, feedback, and/or mentoring since last performance appraisal
- Examples of the employee's "product" (eg, patient medical record, accounts receivables report, or radiographic image)

The employee should also be given an opportunity to prepare for the face-to-face meeting. In most cases, 2 weeks' notice is sufficient. The invitation should be issued in person by the manager and a date and time agreeable to both parties selected. The employee should know this is a process all employees will take part in, be given any suggestions for preparation, and have any procedural questions answered (questions related to the review itself should be answered during the meeting). It may be useful to suggest the employee be prepared to discuss progress on previously set goals, career objectives, job-related problems, ways management could help the employee perform better, and goals for the coming year. The performance appraisal process does not have to be a top down process. Some organizations have found that by involving others in performance reviews, the result is a more holistic

Self Appraisals: Employees rate themselves on a number of criteria and suggest improvements. The manager's role becomes more of a counselor and less of a judge. In such a system, employees tend to feel they have more of a voice in the process compared with traditional reviews. Difficulties arise, however, when there are significant differences between the employee's view and that of the manager. The employee may rate himself or herself harder than the manager does and conclude the manager does not know what the employee does. Alternatively, the employee may fail to see deficiencies, which will not be corrected unless someone else points them out.

360 Degree Feedback: Employees interact with many people in the course of a work day, but a traditional manager review primarily presents only one view of employees' performance. An imaging technologist interacts with patients, nurses, and front office staff; the billing clerk deals more with third party payer staff than with coworkers. A 360 degree appraisal seeks reviews from representatives of all groups involved with the employee. It gives a more well rounded view of the employee's performance; coworkers are likely to understand the challenges of their work. However, such a system requires careful training of all employees on how to give constructive feedback, a significant level of trust among employees, and considerable coordination. It is best used strictly for employee development, not for determining compensation or promotion.

appraisal. Among the most common alternatives to the traditional supervisor appraisal are provided in Box 11.4.

Writing the Appraisal

Having collected stacks of documentation in most cases, the manager now needs to systematically organize the information to produce a fair, accurate, clear, and worthwhile appraisal. The previous year's performance goals can provide structure. For example, if a goal of the receptionist was to improve telephone responsiveness, relevant documentation could include patient complaints about excessive waits, performance log entries related to coaching about answering within 3 rings, and certificate of completion of a telephone etiquette course. The better organized the material, the more organized the final review document.

When reviewing the documentation, the manager may find it helpful to ask questions such as:

- Was the goal or standard of performance achieved? Why or why not?
- What evidence exists to show that?
- If the goal was not achieved, what circumstances prevented it and what needs to happen to achieve it?
- Does the employee have the necessary skills, equipment, etc, to achieve the goal or meet standard? If not, how can the situation be changed?

The answers to these and other questions will lead to conclusions about the employee's past performance and guides for planning future goals. In writing the narrative portion of the review, the manager needs to keep in mind the following suggestions:

- Write a narrative that is:
  - Brief and to the point
  - Complete enough so that someone else could read it and understand the conclusions
  - Accurate
  - Concrete with specific details wherever possible
  - Written in the active voice with the "actor" clearly indicated ("Sue devised a new reception process," not "A new reception process was devised.")
- Begin with general conclusions or statements, then provide specific examples and details to support them.
- Avoid using slurs or language that could be read as biased or discriminatory.
- Use a tone that is respectful of the employee.
- Remain consistent in the appraisal with feedback given throughout the year. If the year end conclusions are significantly different from ongoing feedback, either the manager needs to improve his or her skill at giving feedback or something has caused the employee's performance to change, which should be indicated in the review.

Conducting the Meeting

Setting the Stage

The appropriate atmosphere will contribute significantly to the effectiveness of the appraisal as a performance tool. Adequate time should be available (usually an hour); privacy should be assured and interruptions and distractions avoided. The room should be comfortable, and the manager and employee should be seated next to one another or face-to-face but not on opposite sides of a desk.

The Appraisal Conversation

This will be more of a collaboration if the tone is businesslike but friendly. The manager will want to spend a few minutes in small talk that is genuine; this is not the time to suddenly show an interest in the employee's hobbies, for example. The goal is simply to release some tension and help both parties relax.

The manager should explain any ground rules (eg, confidentiality, no discussion of pay increases) and give the employee an idea of how the meeting will proceed. If the employee has been asked to prepare a self evaluation, this should be discussed first. The employee should be given adequate time to talk and the manager should actively listen, asking questions for clarification when necessary. Then the manager's evaluation should be reviewed and any discrepancies between the 2 appraisals discussed. If the manager's appraisal remains unchanged, the reasons should be explained.

The next step calls for a brief review of the employee's job responsibilities and whether any changes are called for. This is also a good time to ask what could be done to enable the employee to better carry out those responsibilities.

Finally, the manager and employee should agree on a few performance goals for the coming year and discuss any training needs. This may result in a formal development plan or a less formal agreement to identify appropriate training to achieve a particular goal. As discussed earlier, benchmarks and industry standards can serve as starting points for establishing individual goals for measurable activities (eg, procedure rates). This is an appropriate time to once again ask the employee what management can do to expedite goal achievement.

The meeting should end on a positive note, with the manager expressing appreciation for the employee's participation and describing how follow up will take place.

As is often the case in employee relations, the manager's ability to communicate and skill in interpersonal relationships will have a profound impact on the meeting's success (Box 11.5). The manager should:

- Be sensitive to the effect the evaluation is having, reflecting (describing) emotions the employee expresses to build rapport
- Show respect for the process and employee
- Actively listen by taking notes, asking questions, allowing the employee time to speak, and repeating key points
- Be empathetic, especially if the employee's performance is below standard
- Avoid belittling or attacking the employee
- Give positive, constructive criticism when needed that is
  - Straightforward, clear, and direct
  - Specific, to aid problem solving
  - Balanced with comments on good performance
  - Helpful, with concrete suggestions for ways to improve
  - Encouraging, with specific comments about the employee's value to the facility and ability to improve
- Avoid becoming defensive or arguing over differing points of the appraisal; it is advisable to state the 2 views and move on to the next point

As with any conversation between 2 people, a performance appraisal can turn sour. It is important that the manager deal with problems that arise during the meeting, so developmental goals can be achieved. Here are a few suggestions for tackling problem behavior:

Complaining repeatedly without making any suggestions for change: The manager needs to listen to the complaint, acknowledge the employee's feelings, restate the facts involved, and then turn the conversation toward solving the problem.

Unresponsiveness: Employees who sit in silence or respond with a simple yes or no to questions need to be encouraged to participate. The manager should ask open ended questions ("Why do you think that happened?"), sit silently until the employee speaks, and listen carefully with his or her body leaning slightly toward the employee. The manager should also remind the employee that anything said in the meeting is confidential and to feel free to ask questions even after the meeting.

Hostility: When an employee is argumentative or hostile, no progress will be made, so the manager should first try to get the emotions under control or, failing that, consider postponing the review. By carefully listening, repeating the key facts of the employee's argument, and turning the conversation toward problem solving, the manager may draw the employee into a constructive conversation, with less emotion.

- Show flexibility and a willingness to change the appraisal when appropriate
- Maintain eye contact, smile when appropriate, face the employee, and use gestures to support points

Most important, the meeting should be a dialogue, not a monologue. Ideally, the manager will do only about 10% of the talking.[2]

Appraisal Follow Up

The final appraisal document should reflect the views of both the manager and the employee. This can be achieved either by attaching the employee's evaluation and/or comments to the manager's review or preparing a single evaluation form that incorporates comments from the meeting and a summary of both parties' appraisal. The document should also note the development plan for the forthcoming year. The employee should sign the final document as an indication that it is an accurate description of the meeting's conclusions, not necessarily that he or she agrees with all the comments. The employee receives a copy and another is put into the employee's personnel file.

Linking Compensation to the Performance Appraisal

Historically, performance appraisal results have been used to determine pay increases and promotions. This is still the case in many organizations, and the review meeting may include a discussion of any change in pay. However, some experts question the wisdom of tying pay so closely with performance and have severed the link.[1,2]

Facilities that agree with this view focus the appraisal meeting on performance and hold a second meeting to discuss promotions and pay increases.

DelPo lists the following negative consequences as resulting from linking pay to performance[1]:

- Employees are less forthcoming in their feedback.
- Employees may be less willing to aim for ambitious goals or take on "risky" assignments, fearing failure may affect their pay increases.
- Managers may write the appraisal to support a predetermined pay raise and may not accurately reflect performance.
- Employees tend to focus on the financial aspects, giving less attention to the development plans.

Others have cited the disconnect that occurs when salary budgets are limited or raises are set at a predetermined, fixed percentage or amount. In such instances, managers are unable to adequately reward high performing employees and morale declines.[2]

As a heavily regulated and often capitated business, healthcare faces just such circumstances. Budgets are tight and finding resources for pay raises can be difficult. As detailed in Chapter 7, most healthcare organizations have a pay system that rewards individual employees based on years of experience, service to the organization, and their educational backgrounds. The system usually establishes a minimum and maximum pay level and uses a formula to compute a prospective employee's starting salary within the pay range. Employees gradually move toward the maximum range with years of service and positive performance appraisals. The healthcare organization established a range, usually 3% to 5%, within which the employee's pay may increase each year until the maximum is reached or ranges are realigned. The human resource staff will determine the appraisal process and scoring scale used, and in some cases the senior management will set the amount of the raise allowed.

To overcome some of the negative consequences inherent in the traditional pay-for-performance (or merit pay) plans, some organizations have implemented a new pay-for-performance process. It establishes performance standards for awarding different amounts of merit pay for different performance levels. This system allows leaders of imaging facilities to reward superior performers with larger merit increases than their colleagues. Criteria include technical, nontechnical, clinical, and nonclinical aspects of performance, based on the job. These measures of quality are tied to the organization's mission, values, and goals. The employee receives a score for each performance category; the overall score determines the merit pay increase, usually set by human resource staff or senior management.

Employees are given their own portfolios, within which they record work improvements, work performance, and evidence of rewards and recognition. The portfolio enables employees to document and organize their year long performance and becomes the cornerstone of the annual appraisal review. The portfolio is reviewed in detail and all performance improvements, strengths, and weaknesses are discussed.

The beauty of this type of job appraisal is that it is more than just a clinical and technical appraisal. It takes more than clinical and technical skills to be a top performing team member or employee. For example, excellent technologists are not only highly skilled in the technical aspects of their job but are also resourceful, customer friendly, dependable, team oriented, compassionate, caring, and sensitive. Pay for performance allows those positive values and behaviors that are important to the organization to be included in the evaluation process. Top performers are expected to demonstrate all of the important technical and clinical skills but also other behaviors, values, ethics, and morals that are equally important in creating a well rounded, top performing employee.

Conclusion

All employees want to know that their job performance is valued by the organization. Constant and consistent feedback is essential for improving and maintaining desired performance. Managers who invest the time to ensure that excellent performance is recognized and poor performance is corrected will spend less time overall with staffing and performance issues. No matter what type of appraisal system is used, constant feedback must occur because this drives performance improvements; excellent performance that is recognized drives employee satisfaction, which can drive all other organizational goals.

References

1. DelPo A. *The Performance Appraisal Handbook: Legal & Practical Rules for Managers.* 2nd ed. Berkeley, CA: Nolo; 2007.

2. McKirchy K. *Powerful Performance Appraisals. How to Set Expectations and Work Together to Improve Performance.* Franklin Lakes, NJ: Career Press; 1998.

3. Martin T. Increasing the value of performance appraisals. *Assessment & Evaluation.* September 2006. Available at: http://www.talentmgt.com/assessment_evaluation/ 2006/September/155/index.php. Accessed November 9, 2007.

4. Archer North & Associates. Performance appraisal methods: rating scales. Available at: http://www.performance-appraisal.com/ratings.htm. Accessed November 9, 2007.

5. Jensen J. Employee evaluation: it's a dirty job, but somebody's got to do it. The Grantsmanship Center Web site. Available at: http://www.tgci.com/magazine/ Employee%20Evaluation.pdf. Accessed November 8, 2007.

6. Archer North & Associates. Performance appraisal methods: results method— management by objectives. Available at: http://www.performance-appraisal. com/results.htm. Accessed November 9, 2007.

Chapter 12

Coaching, Counseling, and Mentoring

Ed Yoder

Coaching, counseling, and mentoring are invaluable in retaining the type of staff that ensures patient satisfaction and safety and helps the organization achieve its goals. Coaching aims to develop all employees on an ongoing basis through training, role modeling, feedback, and designing jobs that empower employees. For poor performers, counseling offers guidance that leads many of them to change their behavior, improve their performance, and remain on staff. Finally, a manager who mentors a top performing employee or colleague by providing support, challenging the individual to grow professionally and think creatively, and helping clarify his or her vision will be rewarded by the development of an employee capable of assuming increasing responsibility within the organization and the profession.

As has been emphasized throughout this book, healthcare is a labor intensive business, dependent on the performance of people. The imaging administrator's ability to lead and manage people, which is fundamental to the success of any imaging facility, depends heavily on the techniques of coaching, counseling, and mentoring. Although managers may use these terms interchangeably, there are in fact differences among the techniques, particularly with regard to application and purpose.

Coaching, Counseling, and Mentoring: When to Use and Why

Benefits of Coaching

Coaching is the technique of continually developing all employees. It starts with hiring the right person for a job and continues with an effective orientation, performance appraisals, and assessments of training needs designed to close any existing skill gaps or update with new skills. Stone has described the process as one "by which employees gain the skills, abilities, and knowledge they need to develop themselves professionally and become more effective in their jobs."[1]

Coaching is applied to all employees and involves ongoing feedback, training, positive reinforcement, and designing jobs to increase employee empowerment.

An effective manager-coach can boost employee performance levels and increase rapport with and decrease complaints from employees. Performance reviews are likely to be less stressful, as the feedback employees have received throughout the year eliminates any unpleasant surprises. Coaching increases an employee's employability and provides the skills to take on more challenging assignments. This leads to greater job satisfaction and performance and builds employee loyalty and respect. It also produces employees who are capable of taking on additional responsibilities that may lighten the imaging administrator's workload.

Benefits of Counseling

Admittedly, not all employees will respond to coaching in a positive manner. A poor hiring decision may result in a poor match between an employee's skills and the job's requirements; employees lose motivation and do not respond to efforts to revitalize it; an employee's personal problems may lead to performance problems. When coaching fails to turn a poor performer around, counseling is the next step. This is a one-on-one process during which the imaging administrator and employee agree there is a discrepancy between expected and actual performance; identify the source of the problem; and agree on a solution that will improve performance. Counseling is reserved for employees with ongoing performance or attitude problems, such as chronic tardiness, repeated failure to meet deadlines, lack of cooperation, and disrespect of patients.

Low performing staff members are a burden to any business. If left unaddressed, their attitudes and activities can cause high performing staff members to leave, result in patient dissatisfaction, lower morale and motivation of fellow employees, and consume too much of an imaging administrator's time and attention. Counseling may help some low performers become at least acceptable employees; it shows other staff members that management recognizes a problem exists and is attempting to address it; and if all else fails, counseling prepares the way for eventual termination.

Benefits of Mentoring

Managers who spend their days in countless meetings, preparing reports, and searching for ways to meet budgets and workforce plans can easily overlook the needs of their best performing employees. But these high performers are invaluable to a facility and potentially to the profession and deserve attention beyond coaching. It is to these top staff that mentoring is directed.

Mentoring involves "dynamic, reciprocal, personal relationships in which a more experienced person . . . acts as a guide, role model, teacher, and sponsor of a less experienced person."[2] The word *mentor* comes from Homer's epic poem *The*

Odyssey, in which Odysseus entrusts his son to the care of his friend Mentor, during the father's long absence in battle and adventure. Mentor was teacher, advisor, guardian, friend, coach, and father figure to the young man, roles reflected in the modern day application of the term.

A successful mentoring relationship benefits the mentee, the mentor, and their employer(s). According to Johnson and Ridley, mentees can experience the following benefits, compared with nonmentored peers[2]:

- Better rates of promotion
- Higher salaries
- Accelerated career mobility
- Greater professional competence and identity
- Increased career satisfaction
- Decreased job stress

Mentors experience tangible and intangible benefits as well. A survey of senior level hospital administrators found that 96% were motivated to mentor junior level executives by personal satisfaction, but nearly 16% expected increased pay and 18% anticipated bonuses based on their participation in a mentoring program.[3] Mentors also experience career rejuvenation and enhanced creativity as they are stimulated by the mentee's questions and motivation. If the mentor is the mentee's manager, as the mentee is able to take on greater responsibility, the mentor can transfer projects to the mentee and enjoy less job stress.

Organizations that encourage mentoring either as informal, ad hoc relationships or through more formal matching programs also benefit from the one-on-one communication, attention, and education the process encourages. Mentored employees are more likely to remain on staff and are highly motivated. Their learning curve is shortened, increasing productivity. Protected by the mentor, they may be more willing to think innovatively and take part in challenging projects that carry some risk of failure but promise significant rewards to the organization. Other employees who view the mentoring as demonstrating management's interest in employees beyond the immediate "what can you do for us today" may be more likely to remain on staff and increase productivity to gain mentee status. If the mentee is able to communicate staff concerns to the mentor-manager, potential problems can be dealt with quickly, before they impact patient service or productivity.

The skills and behaviors needed to effectively coach, counsel, and mentor employees are the focus of the rest of this chapter.

Becoming an Effective Coach

Effective coaching is as much about an attitude as it is about behavior. Managers who coach their employees believe most of them want to advance within the organization and their profession and to do their jobs well. It is the manager's job to help their employees achieve, develop professionally, and enhance job performance by creating a work environment that supports and encourages learning, independent thinking, and contributing to the business (Box 12.1). Stone summarizes the duties of a coach to include the following[1]:

- *Acting as a role model:* Being a positive role model provides employees with behavior to emulate. Without the manager having to tell them, they learn what is expected of them (eg, showing respect for patients and being honest with coworkers). Consistency between the manager's behavior and the facility's values also helps build employee trust, an essential element to ensure employees respond to coaching as an aid to development and not as rebuke.
- *Clarifying expectations:* Employees cannot meet performance objectives that are not spelled out to them. The coach-manager must be specific about both the requirements of the job and the organization's expectations for the unit and all employees related to the overall strategy and mission. Lack of information leaves employees frustrated and demoralized.
- *Providing feedback on behavior that enhances performance:* Feedback is one of the most crucial elements of coaching. Ideally, feedback is given as a particular behavior occurs—positive feedback to reinforce desired behavior, negative feedback to change behavior—in private and in a nonjudgmental manner (see Sidebar 12.1).
- *Hiring qualified employees:* Developing employees to their full potential starts with hiring the best available people. In particular, coach-managers look for people who have demonstrated an eagerness and ability to learn new skills, a need for challenges in their work, and a willingness to challenge existing practices and suggest alternatives.
- *Carrying out performance appraisals that encourage employee development:* Too often, performance appraisals are viewed as a chore to be gotten through as quickly as possible; they focus on an employee's failures and how they affect compensation. The coach-manager, however, sees these annual appraisals as an integral part of an ongoing effort to develop staff members and an opportunity to discuss ways for the employee to meet or exceed performance standards for the forthcoming year.
- *Providing training and other resources to support employees in performing their jobs well:* Each employee should have a career development plan from which training needs

Box 12.1 Coaching Inventory

Scale: 1 = almost always; 2 = usually; 3 = sometimes; 4 = rarely

To what extent do you:

_____ 1. Let people know on a regular, informal basis how they are doing?

_____ 2. Make an effort to provide people with immediate feedback for their performance (both positive and negative)?

_____ 3. Take the time to observe specific behaviors of your employees?

_____ 4. Know the career goals of your employees?

_____ 5. Take time for casual conversation with your employees?

_____ 6. Know enough about the personal lives of your employees to understand the impact on their work performance?

_____ 7. Feel comfortable disciplining an employee for continued unacceptable performance?

_____ 8. Feel comfortable personally confronting an employee about behaviors you think are inappropriate or counterproductive?

_____ 9. Know what each of your employees is most proud of?

_____ 10. Build individual relationships with your employees?

_____ 11. Illuminate employees' strengths and weaknesses so that they can see them for themselves?

_____ 12. Listen to your employees about their feelings, ideas, or concerns?

_____ 13. Assist employees with ways of building on their strengths and improving areas of weakness?

_____ 14. Feel comfortable acting as an impartial listener to an employee with a personal problem?

_____ 15. Think that your employees believe that you act in their best interest?

_____ 16. Adapt your coaching style to meet the specific skill level and need of your individual employees?

_____ 17. Build strong teams with employees who have complementary strengths?

_____ 18. Set realistic targets and goals for individual employees as well as for your team?

_____ 19. Encourage your employees to take personal and team responsibility for stewardship for getting the entire job done?

_____ 20. Encourage people to use their strengths to compensate for their weaknesses?

_____ **TOTAL**

If your score is ...

20 to 30: You exhibit coaching behavior. You do a good job of letting people know where they stand, encouraging employees to excel, and building the kinds of relationships that enable you to successfully lead your team.

31 to 55: You exhibit moderate coaching behavior. At times you provide employees with the kind of guidance they want and need, but you are hesitant to confront and delve deeply into the tougher issues and concerns of your people. Make more of an effort to get to know your staff.

56 to 80: You exhibit low coaching behavior. You may be too involved with getting the job done—you may have to stop "doing" so much and start "being" more. Leadership involves knowing the people who report to you on more than a superficial level. Until you do this, you will only be able to manage and not lead.

Source: Frankel LP. Employee coaching: the way to gain commitment, not just compliance. _Employment Relations Today._ 1992 (summer). Available at: http://www.drloisfrankel.com/articles.section/stories/datafiles/employeeCoaching.pdf. Accessed December 3, 2007.

SIDEBAR 12.1: How to Give Feedback

The differences among criticizing, giving advice, and offering feedback are significant. Criticism is judgmental and implies the employee is wrong or bad. Whether intentional or not, criticism tends to damage self-esteem, generate defensive behavior, and lessen the likelihood of change. (Does nagging ever really achieve change?) Giving advice, especially if unasked for, draws resentment from the receiver of the advice and again generates defensive behavior. It also prevents employees from learning to solve their own problems and make their own decisions.

When done well, feedback provides information based on the employee's own statements and knowledge that can be used to make decisions and solve problems. It may include insights from the manager's experience, but does not tell the employee that he or she is wrong. To give useful feedback, the manager should:

1. Listen carefully as the employee describes the problem and/or observe the behavior in question.
2. Feed back any emotions or information the employee expresses to ensure no misunderstandings.
3. Ask open ended questions to elicit additional information.
4. Use body language and tone of voice that signals a willingness to help (not punish). The attitude, either expressed or implied, should be that the employee would have eventually recognized and corrected the problem himself or herself.
5. Provide feedback about performance in a straightforward, honest way, but with empathy.
6. Focus on behavior that can be changed and demonstrate what should be changed, where possible.

can be assessed. As coach, the manager needs to help employees identify and access the most appropriate training, based on the employee's learning style, base of knowledge and experience, and the available resources. Whether the training involves one-on-one demonstration, self-directed review of a manual, or a formal course, the manager should follow up to ensure the desired result has been achieved.

- *Creating a work culture that encourages employee initiative and motivation:* Employees are motivated when (1) the organization's goals, vision, and mission are clearly communicated; (2) employee efforts are recognized; and (3) employees are encouraged to identify their internal motivators and helped to achieve their career aspirations. Initiative is nurtured when employees are involved in decision making, asked to solve problems, and are not penalized for honest mistakes or when suggestions do not achieve the desired results.

- *Praising regularly and often to achieve desired performance levels:* Praise, a critical element in motivating employees, is by nature a positive experience. To be effective, it should be sincere and concise and relate to a specific behavior or action.

It should not be accompanied by negative comments (eg, "You did a great job this time, unlike that last project.") or given unenthusiastically or as an offhand remark. Even the busiest manager can find moments to give praise, which is appreciated by low and high performers alike.

Developing Coaching Skills

Probably no skill is as important to coaching as listening, yet few managers receive training in how to listen well. A good listener is genuinely interested in what is being said, shows empathy (not necessarily agreement) with the speaker, and wants to understand any underlying message(s). Listening well helps a coach-manager collect valuable information on which to base decisions, plan training, and provide feedback.

Good coaches are good communicators. They keep employees informed; they are clear, concise, and specific when giving instructions, feedback, and praise. They work at keeping lines of communication open with their staff and senior management. They are also able to ask open-ended questions that encourage communication and employee involvement. Open-ended questions call for responses that explain and provide information, whereas closed-ended questions simply elicit a "yes" or "no" response. Open-ended questions frequently start with who, what, when, where, how, or why (eg, "Why do you think this happened?") or ask for explanations (eg, "Please tell me what happened.").

Because training is fundamental to coaching, good coaches must be able to provide instruction, both in individual and group settings. This skill includes helping employees assess their competency gaps and create a career development plan to fill in those gaps. As mentioned before, training must take into consideration the individual's learning style, so the coach-manager must be skilled at demonstrating a specific behavior, giving background information as appropriate, imparting information to larger groups, facilitating group learning, and tailoring instruction to the employee's experience and skill level.

A good coach is able (and willing) to explore options and to involve employees in the exploration. This requires that the manager maintain an open mind about the best way to solve a problem or carry out a project, listen to suggestions, and weigh alternatives. This coaching behavior helps employees hone their problem solving skills, think critically, and use their creativity constructively. It encourages employee involvement, which in turn builds engagement and ownership. A coach-manager who considers a wide range of options also takes full advantage of the diversified workforce and its wide range of experience and viewpoints.

Following is an example on how coaching can help a behavior multiply. John, a diagnostic imaging technologist, took it upon himself, after completing each patient's examination, to hand out a hospital appointment card with his name and extension on the back of it. He told his patients if they had any concerns, issues, or questions at any time to give him a call. John soon began receiving periodic telephone calls. More important, the patient surveys began to mention John by name and noted how caring he was, how compassionate he was, and how he provided the patients with information. One patient wrote, "Just knowing he was there and would answer questions during the exam was very comforting; when I return I want John to be my technologist and I will ask for him." Very powerful statements from a very satisfied customer! The administrator told John about the patient comments and praised his initiative and thoughtfulness. She also asked him to explain his technique to the other technologists at the next staff meeting, where she again praised his performance and how patients are recognizing him as a "star" performer. She had business cards made up for each technologist and made a point of recognizing an employee as he or she began using the cards with patients. Coaching gave a high quality employee deserved recognition, encouraged less motivated employees to improve their performance, and wired a desired behavior into the department's culture.

When Counseling Becomes Necessary

An employee who is uncharacteristically rude to a patient may respond to coaching, revealing a stressful personal problem and seeking aid from the Employee Assistance Program (EAP) to prevent a recurrence (Box 12.2). However, managers occasionally face employees who fail to meet performance standards despite training and other coaching or who violate employment rules. In such instances, counseling is called for. The facility's human resource manual may specify the required steps and procedures.

Box 12.2 Counseling for Personal Problems

In her book, *The Art of Mentoring*, Shirley Peddy advises against counseling employees or mentees on personal problems unless licensed to do so. However, personal problems have a way of becoming work performance problems, so they should not be ignored. Peddy suggests a 5 step process:

1. Focus on the impact the problem is having on the employee.
2. Listen and ask thoughtful questions, designed to help the employee think through the problem, perhaps from another perspective.
3. Ask open-ended questions designed to help the employee clarify the issues.
4. Help the employee develop a list of options, making suggestions if asked.
5. Provide referrals to qualified professionals or the organization's Employee Assistance Program (EAP), if needed.

Source: Peddy S. *The Art of Mentoring: Lead, Follow and Get Out of the Way.* Houston, TX: Bullion Books; 1998.

These may vary depending on whether the infraction involves a rule violation or a performance issue and on its seriousness.

Counseling for Rule Violations

Generally, counseling for a rule violation or general misconduct will include the following steps:

1. Issue an oral warning, especially if the infraction is relatively minor or is a first offense. This warning is an opportunity to tell the employee what is wrong (eg, he was late and failed to notify his supervisor) and that he or she should not repeat the infraction. It may be appropriate to remind the employee of the impact of the behavior on coworkers or patients.

2. Issue a written warning for a repeat offense or somewhat serious infraction. This memorandum spells out the offense(s), what is expected to correct the situation, and what the likely consequences will be for failure to act. A copy is given to the employee and another is put into the employee's personnel file.

3. Issue a reprimand, the final warning before suspension or termination. This may be the first step in counseling an employee who has committed a moderately serious infraction for which only one "second chance" is possible (eg, violating patient privacy in a way that did no harm to the patient). In the case of a less serious infraction (eg, repeatedly arriving late to work), the reprimand may follow several warnings and offers a last chance for change. In some organizations, this and subsequent steps are carried out by a human resource representative or senior manager.

4. Suspend the employee. Time away from the job provides an opportunity for the employee to evaluate his or her desire to remain employed by the facility and the necessary changes to do so. The suspension should be issued in writing and include the reason, duration, and the procedure to follow to return to work. The facility's human resource policy will specify whether the suspension is with or without pay.

5. Termination, which may be the first (and only) step in the case of serious misconduct (eg, theft of office computers or callous disregard for patient safety). In instances of less serious infractions, termination is the final step in this 5 step process and acknowledges that the employee has been unable or unwilling to change the unacceptable behavior.

Counseling for Poor Performance

Dealing with poor job performance usually calls for a slightly different process. Misconduct is frequently a deliberate act, whereas an employee's low performance may reflect a need for additional training, a change in job responsibilities for which the employee is poorly matched, or other circumstances not entirely within the employee's control (see Box 12.3).

Box 12.3 Identifying the Source of Problems

To effectively counsel an employee to elicit change in behavior, the manager should try to identify the source of the problem. These can include:

- Stress
- Unclear priorities
- Poor time management skills
- Inappropriate level of supervision
- Interpersonal conflicts
- Perceived (or actual) inequities or the organization's failure to live up to promises
- Personal problems

Among the techniques to identify the source during a counseling session are to:

1. Ask open-ended questions that elicit emotions and information.
2. Paraphrase the employee's remarks to ensure understanding.
3. Give the employee the chance to explain without interruption.

Nevertheless, low performers affect customer service and employee morale and reflect negatively on the department. They are generally unhappy with the organization, do not believe in its mission, and rarely support its goals. Such employees seldom do more than is expected and often do not perform up to the level of their capabilities. These individuals can consume a lot of a manager's time because they are often the ones in the manager's office complaining or requiring counseling for a job performance issue.

The performance counseling process begins with an oral counseling session, which should be guided by the facility's human resource policy and procedure manual. In his book, *Hardwiring Excellence*, Quint Studer describes the content of these conversations, using the acronym D-E-S-K, which stands for Describe, Evaluate, Show, and Know.[4] Studer suggests these conversations begin with a description of the behaviors that must be changed or improved. The focus is on the offending behavior, not personality, and the discussion should provide specific examples (eg, "You have failed to complete the monthly accounts receivables report on time during 3 of the past 7 months").

The conversation then moves to evaluating the current situation. This may include details, if appropriate, about the impact of the behavior on coworkers and the department's performance. Now is the time to remind the employee about previous conversations about the behavior, any previous promises to change, and what had been agreed on to resolve the issue.

Although previous discussions should have made the desired behavior clear, it is advisable to once again show the employee what the desired behavior looks like. This may include demonstrating the behavior at the employee's workstation, providing written step-by-step instructions, or orally describing what is expected. The goal is to eliminate any possible confusion for the employee and forestall the future excuse "I didn't know" or "I didn't understand."

Finally, the conversation ends by letting the employee know the consequences of further/repeated violations or continued undesired behaviors. There should be no ambiguity about the results or the timeframe within which the change must be made. To ensure understanding, it may be advisable to ask the employee to repeat the expectations, timeframe, and consequences. Also, as with counseling employees for rules violations, the manager should make detailed notes about the conversation and keep them on file for possible future action.

If low performing employees are allowed to continue their poor performance, they will drag down their better performing coworkers. The resultant dissatisfaction may lead top performers to look for employment elsewhere because they begin to feel that they are expected to carry the department, perform more work than others, and are underappreciated by management. This leads to believing that the system is not fair and those who do not pull their weight within the team are not chastised.

If this oral counseling session and subsequent demonstration fail to pull the poor performer up to standards, a written warning is issued, preferably in a meeting in which the manager and employee once again review the plan for improvement, discuss the continued failure, and explore additional options to achieve acceptable performance. A written summary of the meeting, along with the written warning, is put into the employee's personnel file.

Poor performers may be given an opportunity that those being counseled for misconduct are unlikely to experience—that of transferring or being demoted. Imaging departments within major medical centers or other large healthcare organizations are most likely to be able to offer this option to an employee who continues to perform below standards. In another setting, working with a different boss or carrying out new job tasks that better match their skills may be the catalyst that brings these poor performers up to standards.

If a transfer is not available, the employee may be willing to accept a demotion rather than face termination. If the employee's job were redesigned, for example, with fewer responsibilities (and lower pay), would he or she then be able to meet deadlines and produce accurate reports?

With the tight labor market in some regions and a shortage of imaging technologists, termination may not be considered an option. Keeping a disgruntled or consistently poor performing employee, however, will demoralize the entire unit and could impact patient satisfaction, financial goals, and reviews by accrediting bodies.

Throughout the counseling process for both misconduct and poor performance, the manager should fully document all steps taken, the employee's response, agreed on next steps, and time lines. In addition, human resource staff should be consulted to ensure all legal requirements are met.

Mentoring Star Performers

Within an imaging organization, individuals will occasionally be identified who exemplify the best in an employee. They show initiative; they regularly meet or exceed performance standards; they show a commitment to the profession and their career beyond their immediate position and employer. These star performers are prime candidates for mentoring. Other possible candidates are employees who demonstrate capabilities in several areas but are less competent in 1 or 2 key areas.

Although formal mentoring programs will match employees working in the same organization (and perhaps even the same department), informal mentoring is just as likely to pair 2 individuals who have similar career paths in different facilities. For example, a certified imaging technologist who would like to move into administration might seek a mentoring relationship with an imaging administrator at a hospital-based imaging department in another city whom she met at a conference. However, an experienced imaging administrator may offer to mentor a talented subordinate.

As Figure 12.1 depicts, formal mentoring programs tend to focus on the organization's goals, whereas informal pairings tend to favor the mentee's goals. The more long term the relationship, the greater the potential impact on the mentee's career. Ultimately, quality mentoring relationships build character and develop self-esteem and self-image.

One of the early mentoring models depicted an effective mentee-mentor relationship as balancing 3 elements: support, challenge, and the mentee's vision.[5,6] Activities that support mentees include both emotional and professional support and may involve setting clear expectations for projects, providing resources, discussing alternative

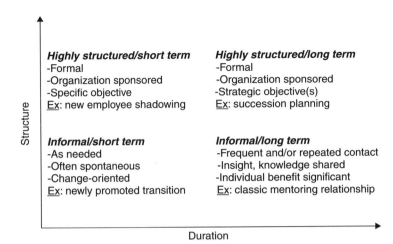

Figure 12.1 Levels of mentoring, based on structure and duration of relationship. Ex = example.

Source: Adapted from Shea GF. *Mentoring: A Practical Guide.* Rev ed. Menlo Park, CA: Crisp Publications; 1997.

responses to problems, and demonstrating trust and respect (Box 12.4). As the mentee gains experience, the level of support generally declines.

Mentors challenge their mentees to encourage higher level thinking and professional growth and development. These activities include questioning mentees' assertions

---

Box 12.4 What Mentors Do

- Set high performance expectations
- Offer challenging ideas
- Help build self-confidence
- Encourage professional behavior
- Offer friendship
- Confront negative behaviors and attitudes without criticizing
- Listen to personal problems (but don't try to solve them)
- Teach by example
- Provide growth experiences
- Explain how the organization works
- Coach their mentees
- Stand by their mentees in critical situations
- Offer wise counsel, rather than just give advice
- Encourage winning behavior
- Trigger self-awareness
- Inspire their mentees
- Share critical knowledge
- Offer encouragement
- Assist with the mentee's career

Source: Adapted from Shea GF. *Mentoring: A Practical Guide.* Rev ed. Menlo Park, CA: Crisp Publications; 1997.

---

and creating opportunities for mentees to demonstrate new skills, take increasing responsibility for their actions, and think about how effectively they handle certain situations. Eventually, mentees learn to challenge themselves.

Vision serves as a way to focus the collaborative activities of both the mentor and mentee. Mentors help mentees clarify their vision by setting realistic goals and articulating what the future will look like. Role modeling and thoughtful conversations about the future are 2 mentor activities that encourage mentees to a worthwhile vision.

Although mentors must be willing to invest time, resources, and thought in the relationship, mentees must show a willingness to learn, be able to communicate well, formulate questions, and listen attentively. He or she must want to work toward an established, longer term goal and to develop his or her skill set. Mentees need to demonstrate both initiative and the ability to follow through on commitments.

Finding a Good Match

In their book, *The Elements of Mentoring*, Johnson and Ridley note that "a substantial body of research finds that mentors and [mentees] who are well matched on important personal and professional dimensions form stronger, more enduring, and more beneficial relationships."[2] Among the traits Johnson and Ridley recommend mentors and mentees share are a sense of humor, social skills, communications style, career goals, work ethic, need for achievement, and level of drive.

An effective mentor is someone who:

- Has strong interpersonal skills
- Is able to communicate expectations
- Is a good listener
- Is willing to be available and accessible to help a colleague advance
- Has contacts within and beyond the facility and is willing to share them
- Is an effective manager who knows how to delegate and to manage people
- Has empathy for others, acknowledging difficulties while giving others credit for being able to overcome them
- Is knowledgeable about the field of healthcare and imaging in particular
- Is generous in offering encouragement, yet unwilling to assume responsibility for the results of another person's actions

Because this is a relationship between 2 people, it is equally important to consider what makes someone a good mentee candidate. To make a mentor's investment worthwhile, a mentee should:

- Have a record of professional success
- Show initiative at work
- Enjoy challenges and be willing to assume greater responsibility
- Be loyal to the organization and share its values
- Be willing to take responsibility for his or her career development
- Be willing to hear feedback, positive and negative, and to learn from it
- Be able to communicate well and articulate needs

Short term mentoring relationships, whether formal or informal, are usually specific to an activity or situation (eg, new employee shadowing). Once the mentee's immediate needs are met, the relationship may remain cordial but not necessarily distinguishable from other professional relationships. A long term mentoring relationship, however, can involve many hours, reflect an intellectual and emotional commitment, and has the potential to profoundly impact the mentee's future. Given its importance, such a relationship should probably begin with an informal or trial period. Perhaps the 2 parties work together on a committee or project. The prospective mentor, having identified someone who might benefit from mentoring, may delegate portions of a project, ask the mentee to suggest solutions to a department problem, or invite the mentee to attend a local meeting of a professional association. If the mentee is not supervised by the mentor and therefore has not taken part in performance appraisal sessions, conversations about career plans or development goals could take place over an occasional lunch or cup of coffee.

Foundations for a Good Mentoring Relationship

Even a relationship between 2 well matched, compatible, intelligent individuals fails, so to increase the likelihood of mentoring success, early stages of the relationship should include conversations that spell out certain key elements of the relationship. Both parties should clearly delineate and agree on the following:

1. *Expectations* about roles, responsibilities, the nature of the relationship, and the types and frequency of interaction (eg, monthly lunch meetings, informal chats as needed, or weekly in-office sessions). Johnson and Ridley suggest that nearly everyone has an "ideal mentor" conceptualization that is usually only articulated when asked for.[2] Comparing ideals is one way to bring inconsistencies in expectations into the open, to be negotiated and agreed on.

2. *Boundaries*, which are important in all mentoring relationships and even more so if the mentor is the mentee's direct supervisor or of the opposite sex. Boundaries need to be set for the type of contact (email, telephone, or face-to-face), venues (home versus workplace), confidentiality, acceptable socializing, and frequency of contact. Both parties should agree on a strategy to apply when the potential for conflict of interest arises (eg, if the mentor is also responsible

for making decisions about the mentee's compensation, one strategy would be to involve a second person in all such decisions.)

3. *Potential benefits and risks* for both parties. An ambitious mentee may only see the upside of being professionally nurtured, but the mentor owes it to the less experienced individual to bring the potential risks to light. Among these are collegial jealousy; "guilt by association" (when either party fails or falls out of favor, the other party suffers as well); and wasted time and resources if either party leaves the organization or relationship prematurely.

4. *Evaluation* of the mentoring relationship. Initially, both parties should agree on a plan for periodic review. Usually, during the relationship's early period, reviews can be useful every 3 to 6 months; as the relationship matures, annual reviews may be adequate. These reviews are an opportunity to elicit feedback from the mentee on the mentor's helpfulness and to evaluate if goals are being met, boundaries are being observed, and expectations are being met. The results can be used to guide the future direction of the relationship.

A mentoring relationship is an evolving one. Thus, while boundaries and expectations should be set early, they will also need to be reviewed periodically as the relationship and its context change. The evaluations provide an excellent basis for these reviews.

Ending a Mentoring Relationship

Even the best mentoring relationship needs to end at some point. Perhaps the mentee has developed beyond the mentor's ability to help. Either party may be offered an opportunity that geographically or organizationally makes continuing ineffective. Less positive reasons to terminate may also occur. The mentee may be overly dependent on the mentor. Either party may find personality conflicts are more prevalent than expected or one party may significantly breach agreed on boundaries or fail to meet expectations. Once trust is lost, the relationship is best dissolved.

Although sometimes the relationship simply ebbs away, the best way to end is with a formal discussion, perhaps over lunch or a cup of coffee. These sessions are ideal opportunities to review the mentee's progress, highlight ways the mentor has benefited from the relationship, and discuss the mentee's future plans. In many cases, it may be appropriate for the mentor to express his or her emotions as the relationship moves to an inactive phase; the revelations provide a model for the mentee to feel free to describe his or her emotions as well. This frees both parties to move on.

Conclusion

The need to develop and retain a motivated, qualified workforce is an ongoing challenge for all healthcare managers and is likely to assume even greater importance as the Baby Boomer generation reaches retirement age. If properly applied, coaching, counseling, and mentoring can have a significant impact on the imaging administrator's ability to staff the facility to best carry out the organization's mission.

References

1. Stone FM. *Coaching, Counseling and Mentoring: How to Choose & Use the Right Technique to Boost Employee Performance*. New York, NY: American Management Association; 1999.

2. Johnson B, Ridley CR. *The Elements of Mentoring*. New York, NY: Palgrave Macmillan; 2004.

3. Finley FR, Ivanitskaya LV, Kennedy MH. Mentoring junior healthcare administrators: a description of mentoring practices in 127 U.S. hospitals. *J Healthcare Manage* 2007;52:260–269.

4. Studer Q. *Hardwiring Excellence: Purpose, Worthwhile Work, Making a Difference*. Gulf Breeze, FL: Fire Starter Publishing; 2003.

5. Provident IM. Mentoring: a role to facilitate academic change. *Internet J Allied Health Sci Pract* 2005;3(2). Available at: http://ijahsp.nova.edu/articles/vol3num2/provident.htm. Accessed September 25, 2007.

6. Doloz L. *Effective Teaching and Mentoring*. San Francisco, CA: Jossey-Bass; 1986.

4 Retention

Chapter 13

Build an Employee Relations and Retention Program

Becky Lamberth

How many people entering today's workforce plan on working for one company until retirement? Not many employees do that anymore. Organizations, and specifically human resource departments, have had to face the current reality of the new workforce and change with the times. In an increasingly competitive marketplace, a good employee relations program can translate into improved employee satisfaction and an increase in morale, productivity, staff loyalty, and retention. Because of this, there is a shift in the culture across many businesses and healthcare facilities. More time and additional resources are being dedicated to establishing programs that help retain qualified staff. New programs consider issues such as staffing and retention, reward and recognition programs, and overall employee well being. How can developing an employee relations program help healthcare facilities? By placing emphasis on their most valuable asset—employees—organizations set the stage for creating an environment that people will want to work in.

Shortages of qualified healthcare professionals continue to challenge healthcare organizations. According to the American Hospital Association, there are 5890 registered hospitals in the United States with 993,866 staffed beds.[1] Studies conducted by the American Hospital Association estimate vacancy rates of 15% for imaging technologists, 13% for pharmacists, and 10% for laboratory technicians.[2] Currently, imaging has one of the highest mean vacancy rates, and it is projected that the demand for imaging services will continue to increase. According to the American College of Radiology, the number of imaging procedures performed continues to increase by a rate of 6% each year, and over the next 20 years imaging procedures will increase from 350 million procedures per year to an estimated 500 million procedures per year. With the increasing number of hospital visits and imaging procedures being performed on patients, it is estimated that an additional 75,000 imaging technologists will be needed to handle the workload by 2010.[3]

The factor that is not fully appreciated is that although length of stay is decreasing, the acuity level of the patient is increasing.[4] As acuity level increases, the need for better trained, more specialized staff also increases. Coupled with the aging Baby Boomer generation (people born between 1946 and 1964), there will be more patients to care for, which will add to the need for additional healthcare workers.[5] It is important to note that while the general population is aging, so too are the health-care workers. The average age of an imaging technologist is 41 years and over 17% of the profession is older than 51 years.[3] The Baby Boomers, at 76 million strong, compose the largest percentage of the healthcare workforce. Baby Boomers are now entering middle age and require more healthcare services, whereas the younger Generation X (people born between 1964 and 1983) contains the smallest pool of entry level workers. Another important element of the workforce shortage is the growth of outside opportunities. Healthcare workers have so many more choices than ever before. As hospitals, outpatient imaging centers, day surgery centers, ambulatory care settings, physicians' offices, and teaching institutions continue to increase in numbers, facilities must compete for the shrinking number of healthcare workers.[4]

Constant hiring, orientating, and training of new employees is inefficient and expensive.[6] Studies indicate the cost of turnover can average 150% of the employee's annual salary.[7] For highly technical or managerial positions, this percentage can be even higher.[6] To put that into perspective, a hospital with a 14% turnover rate in nursing staff would spend more than $5.7 million in 1 year to replace 84 of its 600 critical care nurses.[3] This includes both direct and indirect costs:

Direct costs

- Cost of exit interviews
- Separation/severance pay
- Advertising/recruitment fees
- Interviewing
- Overtime worked by other employees
- Relocation/travel expenses
- Sign on bonuses
- Pre-employment expenses
- Hiring, orientation, and training of new employees

Indirect costs

- Lost productivity
- Decreased employee morale
- Decrease in the quality of care

- Frustrated customers
- Reputation within community

These factors have lead to a real staffing crisis in the United States among health-care workers. To attract new employees, many organizations focus on recruitment incentives including:

- Sign on bonuses. Money can be vital in accepting a position, but not in staying with an organization.
- Tuition reimbursement packages. Many organizations encourage staff to seek higher degrees or additional education.
- Flexible schedules. This is not a new tool for organizations; 10 or 12 hour shifts allow employees flexibility for family life or continuing educational goals.
- Partnering with local universities to entice new graduates. This is an opportunity for employers and for potential future employees to check one another out for a good fit.
- On site child care.

Although these strategies may have successfully attracted employees to the door, the key that organizations need to address is retention.[5]

Keys to Retention

Turnover of employees in an organization can be costly, and not just financially. When employees leave, they take with them their knowledge, skills, and abilities that help contribute to the organization's success.[8] Employee retention is proactively working to keep your employees just that, your employees. A stable workforce creates an environment of efficiency and effectiveness. It is especially difficult if the people that resign are among the top performers in a department. Turnover can result in a loss of productivity and decrease morale for the employees that remain with a facility. Retention is a concern for a large number of human resource directors, administrators, and managers. There are several key points to retention:

- Develop a management team that supports and endorses the employee retention initiatives. Management must talk and walk the mission, vision, and core values of the organization.
- Pay employees well, and then focus on more important things. Salaries need to be competitive and meet the industry standards. If possible, salaries should be linked to the performance of each individual. Managers need to be mindful that while competitive salaries are a key component, it is only one part of the equation.

Imaging technologists ranked "inadequate staffing levels" the primary concern in the workplace, not compensation.[7]

- Treat employees with respect. Employees want to work in an environment of trust and respect.
- Recognize accomplishments. Rewards do not necessarily have to be financial. Rewards with little to no cost are powerful motivators and could be appropriate in certain situations.
- Communicate goals and expectations clearly. Employees need to understand what is expected of them at work. Employees will be unwilling or unable to participate or commit to the organization if they do not know what is expected of them.
- Ask employees for feedback. It is important to involve employees in organization decisions and actively seek their opinions and recommendations. This can be accomplished in several ways, such as informal departmental surveys, open discussions in staff meetings, periodic one-on-one sessions with staff members, or more formalized organizational focus groups.
- Listen to employees' concerns and address them in a timely manner. Follow up is important.
- Share information about the organization. The information should be provided freely and frequently, without the employee having to seek out the information. Provide facts and figures where applicable.
- Provide performance reviews. Employees want praise or feedback so that the skills they bring to the job are recognized.
- Tie pay raises and bonuses to performance.
- Celebrate service milestones. Longevity sets a good example and should be celebrated.
- Offer training opportunities. Training should be seen as a reward for performance. It motivates people by showing them a way to grow, that the organization cares about them, and that they have a future.[9] Various avenues for educational opportunities, including ongoing professional training and cross training, should be provided.
- Promote from within. When promoting an employee into a higher position, be mindful of the need to provide proper training, tools, and mentorship, so that the employee is not set up for failure.

Reward and Recognition Programs

Since turnover can be very costly, in more ways than one, managers need to eliminate, or at least minimize, those costs by understanding the need to retain employees. Shortages of allied health staff make constant recruitment an ineffective method for maintaining workforce levels. To retain staff, employers can begin by developing a culture that includes rewards and recognition within their employee relations program. This will keep qualified staff in the organization.

The first step in creating a program is for the organization to identify a set of core values that embody the company's culture. The core values will serve as the criteria to guide the management staff (as well as the employees) in determining the performance goals and behaviors to reward and recognize.[10] Key examples of performance that could trigger rewards or recognition include, but are not limited to, the following:

- Meeting productivity expectations
- Cost reduction
- Attendance
- Improved safety
- Improved patient satisfaction

Although the organization defines the values that will be rewarded and recognized, the success of the program is dependent on the management team. Training managers and supervisors is critical to achieving the desired outcomes. Before announcing a program to employees, managers should be given key information including:

- How the program works
- Behaviors and performances to be rewarded and recognized
- How to communicate the organization's expectations to employees
- Tools to help motivate employees to achieve the goals

Once established, each program should have a method of measuring successes and identifying components of the program that work and possibly those that need to be changed or eliminated. Successful, established programs will have very tangible payoffs, such as less grievances, increased volunteerism, increase in company profits, decrease in absenteeism, increase in patient satisfaction, and an increase in employee satisfaction.[10] However, measuring the value of newer programs may be more difficult. That is when it becomes more important to solicit feedback from the participants of the program, including both managers and employees.

Developing an Effective Rewards Program

Organizations may spend time and money on developing a rewards program only to find that it is not successful in accomplishing the desired outcome. The objective of a rewards program is to engage, involve, and motivate its employees to satisfy customers and achieve organizational success.[11] Rewards are immediate, appropriate, and personal. It is a win-win situation for employers and employees. Rewarding performance based on the organizational goals provides the employees incentives to work harder. An engaged, involved workforce is a satisfied workforce, and a satisfied workforce is a higher performing workforce.[11] There is little reason to employ a person without taking the necessary steps to make them want to give the organization their best. This can ultimately lead to increased productivity and improved satisfaction for employees, patients, physicians, and other customers of the facility. The reward is about celebrating and recognizing the employee for a job well done.

See Sidebar 13.1 for tips when considering a rewards program.

Steps for developing a successful rewards program include the following[12]:

1. Establish the organizational values and goals that the rewards will be tied to. Set performance standards for employees. What is important to the success of the facility? It can be anything the organization values or strives to accomplish, such as increasing productivity, increasing patient or physician satisfaction, or rewarding staff that voluntarily participate in community service. Not aligning the program with the organization's mission is a common mistake. It is important to note that if the goal requires a change in a current process, additional training may be required to ensure that staff can successfully meet the goals.
2. Choose the correct rewards or incentives. Offering rewards and incentives validates and recognizes outstanding work, but they must be customized to the individual to be effective. Leadership members need to understand what is

---

SIDEBAR 13.1: Tips When Considering a Rewards Program

Key points of a successful rewards program

- Rewards must satisfy individual needs.
- Employees must believe that their efforts will lead to reward.
- Rewards must be equitable.
- Rewards must be linked to performance.
- Do not reward *expected* work or behavior.

Common pitfalls to avoid

- Do not reward behaviors or outcomes that do not support the goals or mission of the organization.
- Do not reward and criticize at the same time.
- Do not overlook anyone.

---

meaningful to each individual.[11] A manager should consider what is valuable to the employee. Also, rewards should not be given to an employee for doing work that is expected of them; they are designated for employees who perform beyond the expectations. The rewards can be financial or non-financial in nature (Boxes 13.1 and 13.2), depending on the behavior and what is most appropriate for each situation. Employers often put too much focus on short term material rewards such as cash bonuses, and not enough investment into creating the right match between the employee's needs and the needs of the organization.[13] Studies show that small niceties such as thoughtful gifts or public recognition (which do not cost employers any money) encourage employees to work harder and better.[10]

3. Communication is critical. Employees should know and understand the goals and behavior that is rewarded. It is important to remember that rewards should be aligned with the organization's goals and missions. By communicating certain goals,

---

Box 13.1 Examples of Financial Rewards

- Bonuses and cash awards
- Promotion or advancement that would increase their salary
- Tickets to entertainment or sporting events
- Payment for professional society membership
- Reimbursement for attendance at continuing education workshops or seminars
- Payment for advanced registry examination fees
- Gift awards such as pins, jewelry, etc
- Financial support for training or educational opportunities
- Expanded workspace or the addition of work support services such as an assistant

---

Box 13.2 Examples of Non-Financial Rewards

- A hand written note of appreciation
- Praise the person in public, such as in a staff meeting
- Offer cross training opportunities
- Provide them with opportunities of more challenging assignments or to develop new skills that could provide promotional opportunities
- Display commendations in the work area such as on the bulletin boards or in the organization's newsletter
- Write a memo and place it in the employee's permanent work file
- Assign them more authority in the department
- Allow them to be mentors for the department
- Have an employee of the month, with such perks as a close parking space
- Grant additional time off

---

employees will be playing an integral role in the organization's overall success. The more managers communicate goals, the more success the organization will have with the program. Leadership must also communicate how employees are nominated and how they are recognized. Formal appreciation typically allows for managers or peers to nominate staff members for exceptional performance. Informal appreciation consists more of daily observations of staff by managers or supervisors.

4. Updates. Keep staff notified of employees who have received rewards and the specific behavior that was deserving of it. Departmental and/or facility recognition of employees inspires others to work harder to achieve similar goals. There are many ways to accomplish this, such as staff meetings, emails, bulletin board notices, and company newsletters.

Developing an Effective Recognition Program

Employee recognition is an effective and inexpensive tool that reinforces and rewards important outcomes that employees create in the workplace. Recognition is about being appreciated, and everyone wants to feel they are appreciated for what they bring to an organization. A well structured recognition program can respond to this need by creating an organizational culture that validates the employee's performance.

Recognizing examples of good behavior and celebrating success are good motivators for employees; however, employers need to avoid common pitfalls and mistakes of rewarding staff, such as rewarding past contributions or recognizing only certain individuals. Linking recognition to current rather than past events helps keep staff focused on the forward strategies and goals of the organization.[11] Focusing on goals helps employees understand that they are indeed directly responsible for supporting the company's mission. For recognition to be effective[10]:

- It must be immediate. Timing is one of the most crucial elements for successfully recognizing employees. Do not let too much time lapse between the behaviors or performance and the recognition for it.
- It must be earned. The behavior or act being recognized should support the organization's mission and goals. Strive for a clear connection between the goals and the accomplishment.
- Emphasize success. Do not dwell on the things that go wrong.
- Deliver recognition openly and publicly, unless that would embarrass the recipient.
- Consistency. Employees should know what behavior merits recognition and that everyone has the potential of earning the praise.

- Frequent praise delivered often enough will continue to reinforce the desired behavior.
- Know your employees. The recognition needs to be tailored to the unique needs of each individual.
- It must be sincere and specific. The employee should know exactly what behavior earned the recognition, and it should be delivered in a personal and honest manner.
- Recognize recognition. Recognize those people who recognize others for excellence in your facility.
- Accountability from management. Organizations need to reinforce the value and importance of recognition programs by holding managers accountable for supporting certain behaviors from employees. Employee satisfaction surveys such as the Gallup Q12 ask the question, "In the last 7 days, have I received recognition or praise for doing good work?"

Employee Assistance Programs

The look of today's workforce is constantly changing. Single parent families, dual career families, and several different generations and minority groups are all part of an organization. Employees struggle with the challenge of balancing a career and family demands. Dealing with this can be difficult and stressful to both managers and employees. A company's responsibility lies in developing an employee relations program that extends to dealing with the stresses and challenges that employees face on a daily basis that can affect productivity, satisfaction, and morale. Part of this strategy is placing increased attention on more formal programs such as the Employee Assistance Program (EAP).

According to the Department of Labor, stress-related physical and mental illnesses can cost a typical company as much as $7500 per worker each year.[14] An effective EAP can help an organization reduce absenteeism, lost time, errors, dissatisfied customers, and medical claims. They can improve production, morale, retention, and public image. This can add up to big dollars in savings for organizations, which can help offset the cost of the program itself. It is estimated that for every dollar invested in a program, the employer can expect to save $5 to $16.

The EAPs are worksite-based programs designed to assist in identifying troubled employees, motivating them to resolve their troubles, and providing access to counseling or treatment.[15] Typically, employers offer EAP services in conjunction with a health insurance plan. However, an effective EAP is more than another employee benefit. It is a comprehensive management tool that supervisors can use to identify and address risky behavior. The programs are intended to help employees deal with personal problems that might adversely affect their personal lives and their work performance. There are 2 EAP models: internal and external.

The internal model (also referred to as in-house or worksite) is operated by the company on-site with their own employee assistance professionals. The counseling sessions occur in an office within the company and all records are maintained on site. The advantages of the internal model include the following:

- Quick and easy access to a professional
- Increased awareness of the program by the managers and employees, which can result in more referrals
- Increased awareness of company problems and issues by the employee assistance professionals

The disadvantages include:

- Perception of decreased confidentiality
- Increased costs of the program for the company

The external model (also referred to as out-of-house or network) is a separate service contracted to a provider not affiliated with the company. The advantages of an external program include:

- Convenience of providing multiple locations for counseling sessions
- Increased perception of confidentiality
- Decreased costs for the employer

Also, many contracted services are more likely to provide a program evaluation and quality control mechanism.[16]

Early EAPs, first introduced in the 1940s, were very basic, modeled after traditional Alcoholics Anonymous (AA) programs (AA was founded in 1935 in Akron, Ohio). The major tenet of AA is that alcoholism is a disease and is controllable. EAPs were a result of the popularity of AA and were initially formed by companies to address occupational alcoholism and mental illness.

Today's EAPs are much more sophisticated and comprehensive. The programs provide an impartial, confidential support service to employees, with services ranging from telephone support to face-to-face counseling or identifying specialists to help. Although EAPs offer help with the resolution of problems that affect work, these problems do not have to be caused by workplace issues. Also, services are typically available to employees and their families. Areas that can be managed by EAPs include:

- Personal issues
- Relationship issues
- Child care and elder care
- Parenting issues
- Substance abuse
- Harassment
- Separation and loss issues
- Balancing work and family
- Financial and legal issues
- Domestic violence

Work-related issues can also be managed by the EAP:

- Stress management
- Time management
- Conflict resolution
- Employee performance
- Assertiveness training

Even with the increased popularity of EAPs, usage rates only hover at 5% to 7%.[17] Reasons behind the underusage of the programs include:

- Because EAPs were traditionally thought of as programs designed to treat substance abuse, employees are hesitant to seek help. In addition, certain generations, specifically workers aged 16 to 24 years, are more likely to engage in risky and destructive behaviors and are less likely to seek help.[14]
- Lack of awareness of services. Programs get lost in the clutter of benefits packages, and management is not well trained in promoting the services available to employees.
- Minorities are less likely to use available programs owing to the social stigma. Certain cultures may have language barriers, may communicate differently, or have certain values or beliefs that may keep them from asking for assistance. As an organization's demographics change, they must ensure their EAPs can address the cultural differences.[14]

Successful EAPs require a strong commitment. Organizations and managers must promote the program and encourage staff to seek assistance. Services should be easily accessible, and employees need to know how to seek services without the knowledge of the organization. Strict confidentiality must be ensured in order for staff to be willing to use the services. Information about the employee is available from EAPs only with the employee's written permission with 2 exceptions: first, the human resource department can request general information regarding the number of services and the types of problems the program addressed, and second, human resource staff and/or supervisors can request information if counseling was required due to discipline problems to ensure the employee is attending mandated sessions and the progress made during the sessions.[15] Finally, the organization should be willing to conduct periodic evaluations of the program's success. There are 3 types of referrals to an EAP:

1. Self referral: employee seeking help for himself or herself
2. Informal referral: a friend or supervisor refers employee to the program
3. Formal referral: employee is referred by the supervisor based on job performance

Conclusion

There are many contributing factors to the staffing crisis being experienced by healthcare organizations. The cost of vacancies and continuous recruitment efforts is both expensive and ineffective for an organization. As the situation continues to worsen, facilities recognize that recruitment does not necessarily translate into retention. Organizations now dedicate financial resources and efforts on creating a culture that promotes employee satisfaction, staff loyalty, and overall morale. An employee relations program, composed of strategies that address the needs of employees both in and out of the workplace, can effectively contribute to a company's overall success.

References

1. American Hospital Association. Available at: http://www.aha.org/aha/resource-center/index.html. Accessed January 15, 2007.

2. Lawson Software, Inc., Healthcare Financial Management Association. Management solutions for combating workforce shortages. *Healthc Financ Manage* 2005;59:suppl 1–8.

3. Williams C, Short B. ACR and ASRT Development of the radiologist assistant: concepts, roles and responsibilities. *J Am Col Radiol* 2004;1:392–397.

4. Upenieks V. Recruitment and retention strategies: a magnet hospital prevention model. *Nurs Econ* 2003;21:7–13,23.

5. Martin U, Schinke, S. Organizational and individual factors influencing job satisfaction and burnout of mental health workers. *Soc Work Health Care* 1998;28:52–62.

6. Dooney J. ROI series: cost of turnover. November 2005. Available at: http://www.shrm.org. Accessed January 8, 2007.

7. AFT Healthcare. Empty hallways: the hidden shortage of healthcare workers. Available at: http://www.aft.org/pubs-reports/healthcare/Empty-Hallways.pdf. Accessed December 8, 2007.

8. Buerhaus P, Donelan K, Ulrich B, Norma L, Dittus R. State of the registered nurse workforce in the US. *Nurs Econ* 2006;24:6–13.

9. Mcguire M, Houser J, Jarra T, Moy W, Wall M. Retention: it's all about respect. *Health Care Manag* 2003;22:38–44.

10. Lambillotte D. Informal recognition, a cornerstone for effective organizations. October 2002. SHRM white paper. Available at: http://www.shrm.org. Accessed December 10, 2007.

11. Welch J, Welch S. *Winning*. New York, NY: HarperCollins Publishers; 2005.

12. Testa B. Rewards relaunch. *Workforce Management* 2006:85(8);39–42.

13. Gale S. Small rewards can push productivity. *Workforce Management* 2002;81(6):86.

14. Ruiz G. Expanded EAPs lend a hand to employers' bottom line. *Workforce Management* 2006;85:46–47.

15. Steffick D, Fortney J, Smith J, Pyne J. Worksite disease management programs for depression: potential employer benefits. *Dis Manage Health Outcomes* 2006;14:13–26.

16. Prochaska S. Employee assistance programs: What does HR need to know? SHRM white paper. Available at: http://www.shrm.org. Accessed December 10, 2007.

17. Wiscombe J. Rewards get results. *Workforce Management* 2002;81(4):42.

Chapter 14

Communication to Improve Morale and Provide Motivation

Becky Lamberth

At one time, the purpose of communication in an organization was to disseminate information. It started from the top and flowed down. However, there has been a dramatic shift in the structure of organizations and within employees themselves. Staff have become increasingly diversified with groups of people in different socioeconomic situations, cultural backgrounds, and value systems. In addition to the complexity of staff, there has been a change in technology. To meet these challenges, leaders need to maintain a culture that focuses on a well developed plan of communication that fits in with the organization's mission and values. Effective communication is a crucial element in decreasing turnover in an already extremely competitive marketplace and in improving the overall financial performance of the organization. Communication must be inclusive, timely, and effective. Managers need to understand the how, when, and why of seeking input from employees, provide feedback on information gathered, and finally, implement strategies for improving the work environment.

Employees want to feel that they are an important part of the organization. By engaging employees, organizations create an environment that empowers the staff to make decisions and to feel invested in the mission of the organization. Engagement can ultimately lead to increased satisfaction (employee, patient, and physician) and better financial performance. Companies cannot be successful over long periods of time without employing energized and engaged employees.[1] So how do employers engage staff? Involve them. It is crucial that organizations share information and get buy-in from staff. Managers need feedback, and employees need to be able to provide a report card on how the organization is performing.

The purpose of communication in the organization has changed. Organizations today tend to be flatter and less hierarchal, so communication with a more horizontal approach is critical for success. Employees want to feel as if they are truly part of an organization and that they contribute to the overall success. To achieve buy-in from employees, they must know what is occurring and this requires effective communication. Employee communication has evolved into a more sophisticated and complex system that fosters 2-way communication: a system that encourages information flowing from the executive level down and at the same time encourages feedback from the staff back to the top. Effective communication systems vary from organization to organization, but they all have a similar end result. Employees know that management listens and management in return is able to use the employee's expertise when making company decisions.[2] Employers committed to providing positive employee communication have seen a decrease in employee turnover and an increase in employee satisfaction and retention. Positive outcomes from successful communication include the following[3]:

- Employee trust in management
- Visibility of the organization's mission and values
- Senior management engagement in communication
- Employee buy-in of the organization's goal and business strategy
- Integration with the reward and recognition program
- Focus on continuous process improvement in the organization
- Employee engagement

Establishing productive communication will ensure that an organization is getting information out to the employees. The strategy developed should fit in with the mission and goals of the organization and will begin at the top. The chief executive officer (CEO) should be the organization's champion and must provide clear evidence in support of communication to the employees. The CEO must be fully committed and serve as a role model for the rest of the management team. In turn, managers must provide consistency and constancy with communication.[3] For communication to be effective, the organization should begin by addressing what information they are seeking, when and how the efforts should take place, and how the organization plans on using the feedback to improve the current environment.

Improving Morale

Communication is the single most important skill of a manager and is essential for high morale. Leaders often confuse staff morale with job satisfaction. They are not the same thing. Job satisfaction is how an employee feels about particular job duties. Employee morale refers to how an employee feels about the company he or she works for. Morale is an employee's attitude about the company and is a direct function of leadership practices. An employee can be satisfied with the job, but still have low morale.[4]

Conflict on key workplace issues can hurt morale and can cause employees to consider changing jobs. Employees have certain expectations from the company that may differ from what the employer can deliver.[4] To prevent this, organizations must have a communication strategy. Communication is the foundation for all actions in the workplace and provides the supervisor an opportunity to build a relationship with the work group. The right interactions are positive and can create the right workplace atmosphere and climate.[5] Effective communication is necessary to understand the needs of staff and should be[5]:

- Multidirectional
- Objective
- Factual
- Comprehensive
- Credible
- Timely

Techniques

It is estimated that managers spend 40% of their time giving and getting information.[6] This means that throughout the course of a day, a manager must be able to effectively communicate lots of information to employees, and, for many, it has become increasingly difficult. Employees are diverse, and each responds differently to various communication methods. Effective communication must be clear, concise, and honest. More important, it should be delivered in a manner that will be received and understood by the employee. Gone are the days when important information could simply be posted on a bulletin board where staff members were sure to see it. Younger, more technologically savvy employees such as Generation X and Millenials are less likely to read and digest information if not done so electronically. That is why it is essential for organizations to incorporate different communication methods, such as:

- Bulletin boards
- Posters
- Newsletters
- Email
- Fax blasts
- Telephone hotline
- Staff meetings
- State of the company meetings
- Intranet
- Face-to-face communications

Providing Motivation

People join an organization for specific reasons and have certain expectations about what they will receive and what they will contribute to that organization. A manager must create an environment in which an employee can motivate themselves to perform well. Motivation is the will to achieve and an internal drive that is present to satisfy unmet needs. It is the desire, energy, or interest that translates to action.[7] For employees, that action is viewed as work performance.[7] Managers are constantly challenged with reducing the workforce and at the same time increasing productivity. To do this, they must understand what motivates people. Motivation can be categorized as intrinsic or extrinsic.[8] Intrinsic motivation is activity performed for one's own personal satisfaction or because it is believed to be important.[9] Essentially, it is working for the love of the job.[8] Examples of intrinsic rewards include a sense of accomplishment or achievement, a feeling of responsibility, or the opportunity to learn something new. This is often credited as the most crucial type of motivation for increasing employee performance and retention. Extrinsic motivation results in actions that are performed to acquire material or social rewards or to avoid punishment.[9] Essentially, it is a reward given to employees contingent on work performance. Extrinsic rewards are tangible and visible to others, such as a bonus or promotion.

Whether staff is motivated by money, power, career advancement, or by the need to fulfill a more personal goal of achievement, people join an organization for specific reasons and with a purpose in mind. Keep in mind that staff can be motivated both intrinsically and extrinsically. It is the manager's responsibility to understand what motivates their employees and reward them appropriately in order to retain the staff and ultimately assist the organization in achieving success.

Techniques and Theories

Motivation comes from within. Managers cannot motivate. What managers must do is to create a work environment that improves motivation. Jobs should provide sufficient challenges to an individual so that it fully utilizes his or her ability. Employees demonstrating increasing levels of ability should be given increasing levels of responsibility. So often, employees are assigned to tasks that do not utilize their talents, abilities, or skill, or they are assigned to the wrong tasks to keep them motivated. The first thing managers need to realize is that what motivates them does not necessarily motivate their staff. They need to recognize what is important to their employees.[5] There are strategies all managers can implement to increase motivation:

- Clearly define expectations and set goals.
- Provide performance feedback.

- Relax tight supervisory rules and delegate decision making authority.
- Provide resources and support so that staff can perform job.
- Be a respected role model.
- Share information.
- Be consistent and fair with all employees.
- Provide training and education to promote professional growth.
- Recruit motivated individuals.

Management ideas and practices have been used since the beginning of recorded history; however, the study of management has only been around for about 125 years.[6] Before the scientific study of the field, there was little thought given to how employees could be motivated to perform better or to produce more effectively. This all changed with the advent of scientific management.[6] Today, there are several different motivational theories that may provide managers with the insight to understand their employees. Many of the theories in use today, such as Maslow's Hierarchy of Needs, Herzberg's Two-Factor Theory, and Vroom's Expectancy Theory, were developed based on American work populations and may not be entirely useful in today's multicultural organizations. Organizations and managers need to be sensitive to ethnic, national, sex, and age differences when trying to motivate employees.

The Hierarchy of Needs

Abraham Maslow was a psychologist who proposed a theory of motivation, commonly referred to as Maslow's Hierarchy of Needs. The needs hierarchy begins with the basic idea that unfulfilled needs are motivators and focuses on people's internal needs. Maslow determined that people experience 5 levels of need[9-11]:

1. *Physiological.* This is the most basic of all human needs—the need for food and shelter. An absence of these conditions is a big demotivator for employees.
2. *Safety/Security.* People have the need to ensure that no personal harm will come to them. By meeting security needs, employers may improve retention.
3. *Social.* This is the human need for acceptance by others, for belonging, friendship, and affection. Once the basic needs are met, employees will desire stimulating interaction with people in the workplace. They will want to belong to a team and feel like they are part of something more important. Managers need to understand that many employees do not ever move past this level.
4. *Self-esteem.* This includes recognition, status, and prestige. At this level, employees care about what others think about them professionally. Good performance appraisals, promotions, and advancements are motivating factors.

5. *Self-actualization.* The need for achieving one's personal best. At this level, the driving force is completely internal. The employee is motivated and satisfied from creating and meeting challenges, empowerment, autonomy, and decision making. The goal is to prove to themselves that they make a difference.

According to Maslow's theory, the lower level needs must be satisfied before moving upward to the next level. As the need is met, a person progresses to the next higher level of need as a source of motivation. However, studies indicate that higher order needs will not motivate people as long as the lower order needs remain unsatisfied.[6]

Herzberg's Two-Factor Theory

Frederick Herzberg examined experiences that satisfied or dissatisfied people at work rather than focusing on needs. Employees were asked to identify a situation at work that was satisfying, and these were labeled as motivating factors. Similarly, they were asked to describe a situation that was very dissatisfying, and these were labeled as hygiene factors. Hygiene factors are considered maintenance factors that are necessary to avoid dissatisfaction, but by themselves do not provide satisfaction. The motivating factors are intrinsic factors and are a result of the work itself. Motivation factors challenge people to grow, contribute to the work environment, and invest themselves in the organization. These factors drive a person to do a good job and include[11,12]:

- Achievement
- Recognition
- Work itself
- Responsibility
- Advancement
- Growth

The hygiene factors are external factors and are not part of the work itself. These factors do not directly affect a person's motivation to work because they do not stimulate growth or development. They include[11,12]:

- Company policy
- Supervision
- Relationship with manager
- Work conditions
- Salary
- Relationship with peers

Vroom's Expectancy Theory

This motivation theory is founded on the notion that people desire certain outcomes of behavior and performance. It focuses on the perception that employees tend to work harder when they believe they have a good chance of getting personally meaningful rewards. This is the most popular theory of workplace motivation because it focuses on all 3 parts of the motivation equation: input, performance, and outcomes. There are 3 constructs to this theory[9,11]:

1. *Valence outcome.* This is the value or importance an employee places on a particular reward. Managers need to understand that what one employee would consider a desirable reward, another employee would dislike.
2. *Expectancy.* This is the belief that effort leads to performance. When the expectancy is strong, employees believe their hard work will result in good performance, so they work harder.
3. *Instrumentality.* The belief that performance is related to rewards. When instrumentality is strong, employees believe that improved performance leads to better and more rewards, so they work harder.

Additional Motivational Theories

There are additional motivational theories that may be more relatable to the diversified staff in healthcare, including the Equity Theory by John Stacy Adams, the Goal-Setting Theory by Edwin Locke, and the Reinforcement Theory. The Equity Theory extends beyond the employee's individual self. Employees compare themselves to colleagues in terms of overall fairness. When they feel they have been fairly treated, they are more likely to be motivated. If they are treated unfairly, then the employee will not be motivated to perform. This theory helps to explain why an employee can be happy and motivated one day and then unhappy and not motivated the next if they learn that a peer is enjoying a better reward.

The concept behind the Goal-Setting Theory is that motivation is determined by goals that employees strive for. To increase performance, goals must be specific and challenging. However, there are limitations to this theory. The goals set by the employee may not align with the goals of the organization, thus affecting performance and motivation.

The Reinforcement Theory states that behavior is a function of its consequences.[6] Essentially, behaviors followed by positive consequences will occur more frequently and behaviors followed by negative consequences (or not followed by positive consequences) will occur less frequently. Managers can motivate with the reinforcement theory by reinforcing desired behaviors, not reinforcing (or rewarding) wrong behaviors, correctly administering punishment at the appropriate time, and choosing a reinforcement schedule.[6]

Communication Tools and Building a Plan

Leaders of the organization need to determine how the staff feels about the company and then create or maintain a work environment that motivates and keeps morale high. As mentioned previously, motivated employees can lead to increased productivity, which will contribute to a company's overall success. There are a variety of tools managers use to determine the level of morale with employees and provide motivation accordingly, including employee surveys and interviews. As a result, management should be able to determine staff satisfaction, identify areas for improvement, and implement a plan.

Employee Surveys and Interviews

Employee surveys and interviewing methods can be useful tools in gathering information about the workforce and the workplace environment. The information that an employer receives from a survey can be useful in developing programs or implementing changes to improve the work environment. Surveys can be used to achieve 3 objectives:

1. Help the organization understand their workforce.
2. Measure attitudes, behaviors, and effectiveness of the management system.
3. Communicate that the organization cares about the staff.

Satisfaction surveys are often short, narrowly focused, and should be frequently administered.[13] There are different types of surveys as well as different methods for administering them, each to fit an organization's particular needs. Traditionally, the content of surveys has covered such basic areas as job satisfaction, compensation and benefits, tools and equipment, and physical working conditions. Today's survey tools cover information concerning business strategies, goal alignment, and customer focus.[14] Management needs to understand that there are several key issues to address when the decision is made to administer a survey. First, management must demonstrate a commitment to the survey. Companies allocate large financial resources to the survey and should reap the benefits; however, the commitment should be more than financial[14]:

- Management must believe the results of the survey.
- They must share the results with employees, even if the results are negative.
- They must take action guided by the results of the survey.
- They must be willing to explain to staff why certain changes cannot be made.

Next, the organization needs to determine what type of survey to use and when to administer it. Surveys should be aligned with the company's goals and should be used to solicit feedback concerning important business decisions. Employers should not waste financial resources or the time of their employees by asking questions that do not support the mission of the organization or collect data that will not force changes that affect the goals of the facility. Climate surveys and employee satisfaction surveys are 2 types of surveys that can be used. A climate survey is intended to gauge the general work environment. This a good tool for companies that are facing large scale change.[15] An employee satisfaction survey drills down deeper and can provide useful insight on individual departments.

Regardless of the type of survey, timing is crucial and should be controlled. An organization should consider the current climate and should time the survey appropriately. Companies should never administer a survey immediately after dramatic changes or when availability of the respondents will be limited.

Finally, organizations need to determine who will administer the survey. Healthcare facilities should avoid developing and administering surveys themselves. Formal surveys require extensive validation to ensure accuracy, and employees should be certain that the information is confidential and that they will remain anonymous. There are many reputable companies that have developed formal survey tools such as the Gallup Organization. In 1999, Gallup conducted in depth interviews with more than 80,000 managers in more than 400 companies. With this research, they were able to develop a 12 question survey called the Q12, for organizations to use to determine employee satisfaction (Sidebar 14.1).

SIDEBAR 14.1: Twelve Question Survey Developed by the Gallup Organization

Q12 Survey

1. Do I know what is expected of me?
2. Do I have the materials and equipment I need to do my work right?
3. At work, do I have the opportunity to do what I do best every day?
4. In the last 7 days, have I received recognition or praise for doing good work?
5. Does my supervisor, or someone at work, seem to care about me as a person?
6. Is there someone at work who encourages my development?
7. At work, do my opinions seem to count?
8. Does the mission/purpose of my company make me feel my job is important?
9. Are my coworkers committed to doing quality work?
10. Do I have a best friend at work?
11. In the last 6 months, has someone at work talked to me about my progress?
12. This last year, have I had opportunities at work to learn and grow?

Source: Buckingham M, Coffman C. *First, Break All the Rules.* New York, NY: Simon & Schuster; 1999.

Regardless of the survey or method type, they should be administered at least once per year through anonymous means. Employees should be comfortable and completely free to be honest and speak their minds. By providing this mechanism for feedback to employees, these instruments will reveal 10 common themes related to engagement for the employer[13]:

1. Pride in employer
2. Satisfaction with employer
3. Job satisfaction
4. Opportunity to perform well at challenging work
5. Recognition and positive feedback for one's contributions
6. Personal support from one's supervisor
7. Effort above and beyond the minimum
8. Understanding the link between one's job and the organization's mission
9. Prospects for future growth with one's employer
10. Intention to stay with employer

Formal surveys are not the only mechanism available to employers to obtain information about their workforce or workplace environment. Interviews, informal and formal feedback sessions, and focus groups are all excellent sources of data. Most people think of interviews only as a means to obtaining a job. However, employers can use interview techniques with current staff. An example of this would be exit interviews.

Feedback is the exchange of information between management and an employee that can be used as a way to motivate, support, direct, or regulate outcomes. Simply put, it is 2-way communication that builds relationships and gathers information. Formal feedback sessions should be scheduled and are more structured, whereas informal sessions are impromptu, on-the-spot conversations that can be just as effective. Focus groups are like interviews, but with more people. Typically, focus groups consist of 8 to 12 people and should be well representative of the organization. Focus groups can be used to gather information, follow up on survey results, or just to check the pulse of the facility.

Determine Staff Satisfaction

Organizations want employees to remain with them. Managers have worked to communicate crucial information regarding the organization's mission and want to get buy-in from staff. A variety of tools, such as surveys and interviews, are used to ask for feedback. Organizational success can be achieved with open communication between the organization and the employees. Managers need engaged and committed staff to ensure this success. So what does all this information say about an organization's employees? What makes them happy and what do organizations need to do to address the needs of their most valuable asset?

Several studies, in and out of healthcare, have been done on job satisfaction of employees. There are as many definitions of job satisfaction as there are variables controlling it.[16-18] A good definition of job satisfaction is "a pleasurable or positive emotional state resulting from the appraisal of one's job experiences as fulfilling important job values."[19] In short, job satisfaction is how an employee feels about his or her particular job duties. It has been theorized that high levels of job dissatisfaction lead to employee withdrawal, particularly in terms of voluntary turnover.[16] What influences some employees to stay while others leave? According to the Gallup Organization, only one quarter of healthcare workers are engaged in their jobs, meaning that only 1 in 4 healthcare employees look forward to going to work everyday.[20] Key variables of job satisfaction that will lead to long term retention of healthcare workers include, but are not limited to:

- Money
- Work environment
- Performance feedback
- Advancement opportunities
- Group cohesion
- Relationships with management
- Demographic characteristics

Identify Areas for Improvement

What do imaging employees need? Consider a few of the questions from the Gallup Q12 survey: Does my supervisor care about me; do my opinions count at work; do I know what is expected of me? These are all functions of the immediate supervisor. Data collected from Q12 surveys clearly show that the single most important variable in employee productivity and loyalty is the quality of the relationship between employees and their direct supervisors. Managers have many hats to wear, and it is no wonder that the relationships between staff and leaders are so critical. A manager's skills directly influence employee attitudes and consequently employee productivity and loyalty.[21]

A common mistake often made by management is the belief that money is a key indicator of job satisfaction. Although money is important and is an area addressed on surveys, job satisfaction depends on much more than simple money issues. Many times, money did not show up in any form in the top 3 reasons for staying with a job or remaining loyal to a profession. However, base salary is not the only consideration in monetary compensation. Benefits such as vacation and sick time (often referred to as paid time off), retirement benefits, and tuition reimbursement are typically part of compensation. Job satisfaction is multifaceted and is influenced by more than just a single element.

Healthcare facilities tend to create very stressful environments because of demands of budget cuts, staffing issues, and diminishing supplies. Imaging professionals express low satisfaction due to a low workforce and unsatisfactory working conditions.[22] Be mindful that imaging technologists display the lowest levels of job satisfaction as it relates to work environment since they often tend to associate a lack of materials and equipment with a lack of sufficient staffing.[20] Employees want to work in an environment of trust and respect, where they feel that they are making a real contribution to the organization. Successful organizations have work environments that foster professional accountability, eliminating stringent rules and allowing more flexibility in decision making, and encouraging an autonomous practice climate.

Implement a Plan

Once an organization has committed to administering a survey and the data have been collected, what are the next steps? It does not do an organization any good to administer a survey if they do not use the data. Employees will expect to see action taken. Data from a survey should aid an organization in creating tools for spurring action plans.[23] Results, both positive and negative, must be communicated as quickly as possible.

Typically, the leaders of the organization are the first to see the data. They will be responsible for implementing action plans as a result of the survey. When evaluating the data, organizations need to determine what changes can be made and which ones cannot. If changes are not possible, that should be communicated with employees along with the reasons. Managers must then begin working collaboratively with employees to solicit feedback on the areas of concern and developing action plans. The action plans need to be communicated and then executed. Senior leadership need to develop specific timelines for implementation and should follow up with managers and employees to measure the success.

Conclusion

Traditionally, organizations were much more hierarchical and disseminated information from the top down. Most employees were content in the knowledge that employment meant a regular paycheck and a pension plan for retirement. Today's workplace has become increasingly flattened, and the workforce comprises a much more diversified staff that demands more from their employers. Healthcare is a competitive arena, and employee retention is dependent on engaged, energized, and satisfied employees. They want to play a much more active role in the success of the organization and need the right tools. Employers are faced with the task of creating a work environment that motivates employees to be more productive while maintaining high staff morale. There are many theories that exist to explain what and how to motivate employees, but it is crucial that managers provide a system that promotes the organization's objectives and core purpose. An effective communication plan can provide the necessary information and tools needed by an organization and the employee.

References

1. Welch J, Welch S. *Winning*. New York, NY: Harper Collins Publisher; 2005.

2. Pomeroy A. Great communicators, great communication. *HR Magazine* 2006:51(7). Available at: http://www.shrm.org. Accessed January 15, 2007.

3. Weatherly L. Organizational communications. SHRM research, 2003. Available at: http://www.shrm.org. Accessed December 12, 2007.

4. Woodward N. Uplifting employees. *HR Magazine* 2007;52(8). Available at: http://www.shrm.org. Accessed January 8, 2007.

5. Roper G. Managing employee relations. *HR Magazine* 2005;50(5). Available at: http://www.shrm.org. Accessed January 15, 2007.

6. Williams C. *Management*. 4th ed. Mason, OH: Thompson Learning, Inc.; 2007.

7. Ellis C. *Management Skills for New Managers*. New York, NY: American Management Association; 2005:24–28, 42.

8. Orr CB, Lockwood NR. Total rewards: Motivating with strategic rewards. SHRM research. December 2006. Available at: http://www.shrm.org. Accessed January 15, 2007.

9. Daniel TA, Metcalf GS. The science of motivation. SHRM white paper. May 2005. Available at: http://www.shrm.org. Accessed January 15, 2007.

10. Sumrow A. Motivation: a new look at an age-old topic. *Radiol Manage* 2003;25:44–47.

11. Nelson D, Quick J. *Organizational Behavior: Foundations, Realities and Challenges*. 3rd ed. Cincinnati, OH: South-Western College Publishing; 2000.

12. Alshallah S. Job satisfaction and motivation: How do we inspire employees? *Radiol Manage* 2004;26:47–51.

13. Vance R. Employee engagement and commitment: a guide to understanding, measuring and increasing engagement in your organization. HR SHRM Foundation, 2006. Available at: http://www.shrm.org. Accessed January 8, 2007.

14. Pardue H. Competing for talent: Creating a work climate through employee surveys to attract, motivate and retain high performing employees. SHRM white paper, 2002. Available at: http://www.shrm.org. Accessed December 12, 2007.

15. Connelly B. Developing and delivering climate surveys and employee satisfaction surveys via corporate internet. SHRM white paper, 2002. Available at: http://www.shrm.org. Accessed December 12, 2007.

16. Lambert E, Hogan L, Barton S. The impact of job satisfaction on turnover intent: a test of a structural measurement model using a national sample of workers. *Soc Sci J* 2003;38:233–250.

17. Lopopolo R. The relationship of role-related variables to job satisfaction and commitment to the organization in a restructured hospital environment. *Phys Ther* 2002;82:984–999.

18. Virtanen M, Kivimaki M, Vahtera J. Selection from fixed term to permanant employment: prospective study on health, job satisfaction, and behavioral risks. *J Epidemiol Community Health* 2002;56:693–699.

19. Steinhardt M, Dolbier C, Gottlieb N, McCallister K. The relationship between hardiness, supervisor support, group cohesion, and job stress as predictors of job satisfaction. *Am J Health Promotion* 2003;17:382–389.

20. Blizzard R. Employee engagement: Where do hospitals begin? *Gallop Poll: Tuesday Briefing*; 2003:81–84.

21. McBride EL. Employee satisfaction: code red in the workplace? *Semin Nurse Manag* 2002;10:157–163.

22. AFT Healthcare. Empty hallways: the hidden shortage of healthcare workers. Available at: http:www.aft.org/pubs-reports/healthcare/Empty-Hallways.pdf. Accessed December 8, 2007.

23. Garvey C. Connecting the organizational pulse to the bottom line. *HR Magazine* 2004:49(6). Available at: http://www.shrm.org. Accessed January 8, 2007.

5 Appendices

In this section:

- Appendix I: Sample Table of Contents
- Appendix II: Human Resource Policies

Sample Table of Contents

Employee Handbook
XYZ Company

FOREWORD

RECEIPT FOR EMPLOYEE HANDBOOK

A. INTRODUCTION

1. Equal Employment Opportunity Policy Statement
2. Non-Discrimination and Anti-Harassment Policy
3. Americans with Disabilities Act Policy Statement
4. Conflict of Interest and Outside Employment Statement
5. Confidential Nature of Work

B. EMPLOYMENT

1. Initial Employment Period
2. Employee Categories
3. Transfers and Promotions

C. COMPENSATION

1. Performance Management and Compensation Programs
2. Performance Management Program Schedule
3. Payment of Salary
4. Overtime Pay
5. Time Records
6. Employee Referral Program
7. Personnel Records

D. TIME OFF

1. Vacation
2. Personal Time
3. Holidays
4. Bereavement Leave
5. Jury Duty
6. Military Leave

---

18. Reference Checks
19. Smoking Policy
20. Tape Recording Policy
21. Tuition Reimbursement Policy

G. LEAVING XYZ COMPANY

1. Resignation
2. Dismissals
   - Immediate Dismissals Misconduct
   - Dismissals Other Than Immediate Termination
3. Post Resignation/Termination Procedures

Source: SHRM, courtesy Proskauer Rose LLP. Available at: http://www.shrm.org/hrtools/policies_published/. Accessed November 7, 2007.

Human Resource Policies

Below is a sample listing of human resource policies that should be present in an imaging facility. For a comprehensive guide with actual sample policies, refer to AHRA's *Radiology Policy and Procedure Manual*.

ALPHABETICAL INDEX

TITLE

Absence, Leave of

Absence, Request for Leave of

Abuse, Substance

Accepting Fees/Pay for Teaching, Consulting, or Providing Services

Access Protection

Access to Hospital Property

Add/Change Position

Add/Change Position, Request to

Affidavit of Auto Insurance (Form)

Age, Minimum Employment

Agency Usage, Employment/Staffing

Aid, Tuition

Appearance, Dress Code &

Application and Employment Process

Application for Tuition Assistance (Form)

Appraisal Form, Performance Planning &

Appraisal System, Job Description/Performance Planning &

Approved Time Off, Paid Time Off

Assistance Program, Employee

Attendance

Attendance Report (Form)

Authorization for Employee Additional Compensation (Form)

Authorization for Employment Expense Reimbursement/Payment (Form)

Authorization to Post or Distribute Information

Auto Insurance (Form), Affidavit of

Background Screening
Badges, Identification
Bereavement Hours, Paid
Birthday Meal, Employee Recognition Programs
Bonus, Recruitment

Call-Back Compensation
Certification of Healthcare Provider (Form)
Checkout List, Employee
Classification, Employment
Clearance, Terminal
Code of Ethics
Code of Personal Conduct
Commercial Motor Vehicle Driver Safety
Communicable Diseases
Community Involvement
Compensation, Call-Back
Compensation, Hurricane/Severe Weather/Disaster
Compensation, On-Call
Compensation, Unemployment
Compensation, Workers'
Compensation for Attending Educational Programs
Compensation Program
Competency of Staff
Compliance Program
Conduct, Code of Personal
Conducting Personal Business during Work Time
Confidentiality
Confidentiality Statement (Form)
Conflict of Interest
Conversion Bank
Corporate Integrity Program: Standards of Conduct for Employees
Corrective Action
Council, Employee
Counseling Form, Verbal
Court Appearances, Jury Duty & Subpoenaed
Credentials
Credit Union

Identification Badges
Immigration and Employment
Insurance (Form), Affidavit of Auto
Insurance, Group Dental
Insurance, Group Health
Insurance, Group Life
Insurance, Liability
Insurance Continuation for Retired Employees, Group Health
Insurance Programs, Disability
Interfacility Work Assignments
Investigation

Job Description/Performance Planning & Appraisal System
Jury Duty & Subpoenaed Court Appearances

Leave of Absence
Leave of Absence, Uniformed Services
Liability Insurance, Professional
Licensure
Life Insurance, Group
Lockers

Mandatory Education Requirements
Meal Periods, Rest
Meals/Entertainment/Gifts
Medical Coverage for Retired Employees Notice & Election (Form)
Medical History Questionnaire (Form)
Medical Leave of Absence
Military Service Leave
Minimum Employment Age
Monitoring (Email/Fax)

Name/Address Change (Form)
New Hires, Starting Rates for
New Position Review (Form)
New Position Review Management (Form)
Non-Employee Orientation
Non-Hostile Work Environment/Harassment
Non-Retaliation

Vendor Relationships
Vendor Support for Education
Verbal Counseling (Form)
Verification of Education (Form)
Visitors/Visiting at Work
Voting

W-4, Form
Warning Form, Written
Weapons
Weekend Differential
Weekend Flex Program: 32/40 & 36/40 Options
Work Assignments, Interfacility
Work, Hours
Work Time, Recording of
Workers' Compensation
Working Undesirable Shifts/Days, Premium Pay for
Written Warning (Form)

403(b) Retirement Savings Plan, Pension Retirement Plan

Source: Winter Haven Hospital, Winter Haven, FL.

Index

Title VII of the Civil Rights Act of 1964, 4, 4s, 5–7, 15
Total compensation, 95, 98s
Toxic chemicals, 13
Traditional health insurance plans, 108
Trainer/facilitator-led training, 149–150, 150b
The Trainer's Handbook: The AMA Guide to Effective Training (Mitchell), 147
The Trainer's Tool Kit (Charney and Conway), 155
Tuition reimbursement, 105, 152–153, 162

U
Ultrasonography, 161
UltrasoundJobs, 55, 57, 57t
Uniformed Services Employment and Reemployment Rights Act of 1994, 112
University Health Consortium, 22
US Bureau of Labor Statistics, 52
US Census Bureau, 21
US Department of Health and Human Services, 20
US Department of Justice, 15
US Department of Labor
    employee insurance data, 108, 109
    impact of stress-related illnesses, 217
    investigations of FMLA violations, 12
    OSHA as agency of, 12–13
    wage/salary data, 101
US Health Care Financing Administration (HCFA), 25

V
Vacation, 105, 110–111
Valence outcome, 229
Violence in workplace, 121
Virginia nurses survey, 40
Vision plans, 109
Vroom's Expectancy Theory, 227, 229

W
Wage and salary
    bonuses, 99

constructing pay ranges, 101–103, 103t, 104, 104f, 105, 105t
    identifying benchmark jobs, 103–104, 104f
    laws governing, 100, 100b
    lump sum merit award, 99
    merit pay program, 99
    overtime pay, 100
    retention bonus, 99
    standard base pay program, 99
    variable pay systems, 99
Watson Wyatt survey, 40
Weddle P, 74
Weddle's Guide to Employment Web Sites (Weddle), 74
Wellness programs, 114
Winning E, 37
Workers' Compensation, 106, 106b, 126
Workforce/staffing plan
    benchmark data for staff utilization, 22, 23f, 24
    as component of strategic plan, 17
    cost of labor, 17
    demand analysis, 22, 23f, 24–25, 25t, 26, 30t
    developing, 17–31
    full time employees, 28s
    gap analysis, 26–27
    independent contractors (outsourcing), 28s
    as living document, 30–31
    part time employees, 28s
    solution analysis, 27–28, 28s, 29–30, 30t
    supply analysis, 18–19, 19s, 20–21
    temporary (contract) employees, 28s
    workforce competencies, 18, 20
    workforce demographics, 18–19, 19s, 20
    workforce turnover and trends, 18, 20–21
"Writing Job Descriptions for Small Business" (Lindner), 34
Wrongful termination lawsuit, 122

Y
YahooJobs, 57